PRACTICAL SUGGESTIONS FOR TEACHING
Edited by Alice Miel

Number 15: Building Children's Science Concepts: Experiences with Rocks, Soil, Air, and Water

---

OTHER TITLES IN THIS SERIES

TEACHING THE SLOW LEARNER
W. B. Featherstone

HOW TO STUDY THE BEHAVIOR OF CHILDREN
Gertrude Driscoll

GUIDING CHILDREN'S READING THROUGH EXPERIENCES
Roma Gans

SCIENCE EXPERIENCES FOR ELEMENTARY SCHOOLS
Charles K. Arey

PUPIL PROGRESS IN THE ELEMENTARY SCHOOL
Willard S. Elsbree

EXPLORING LITERATURE WITH CHILDREN IN THE ELEMENTARY SCHOOL
Jean Betzner

INDIVIDUAL PARENT-TEACHER CONFERENCES
Katherine E. D'Evelyn

REPORTING TO PARENTS
Ruth Strang

PROVIDING DEVELOPMENTAL EXPERIENCES FOR YOUNG CHILDREN
Ada Dawson Stephens

THE GIFTED CHILD IN THE REGULAR CLASSROOM
Marian Scheifele

CHILD GUIDANCE IN THE CLASSROOM
Gertrude P. Driscoll

INDIVIDUALIZING READING PRACTICES
Alice Miel, Editor

BUILDING CHILDREN'S SCIENCE CONCEPTS

Experiences with Rocks, Soil, Air, and Water

MARY SHECKLES
ASSOCIATE PROFESSOR OF EDUCATION
DANBURY STATE TEACHERS COLLEGE

Bureau of Publications
Teachers College, Columbia
New York
1958

© 1958 by Teachers College, Columbia University

Second Printing, 1960

Printed in the United States of America
Library of Congress Catalog Card Number: 58-8243

Editor's Introduction

International developments have heightened the national interest in science. But this new enthusiasm for science will be far from gratifying to science specialists like Dr. Mary Sheckles if it is misdirected. It can be highly gratifying if it calls the attention of the public and the profession to the substantial progress already made in elementary school science education and increases understanding and support of teachers and their advisers as they work to improve the quality of children's science experiences.

To Dr. Sheckles an important goal of science in childhood education is the development of significant concepts on the part of all children. She is convinced that these concepts are built gradually through carefully planned experiences of many kinds rather than through mere book reading or performance of a few dramatic "experiments" with formula and answers provided.

In this fifteenth title in the Practical Suggestions for Teaching series, Dr. Sheckles helps the reader to retrace some of his own science learning and to realize what an extensive science background the ordinary classroom teacher has accumulated. The writer then shows how teachers may help children grow in understanding of basic science concepts which will serve to make their living more intelligent and socially useful. Following this discussion are specific suggestions for helping children discover basic ideas about air, soil, rocks, and water. Teachers are invited to use their own judgment in selecting the experiences which promise to be most useful to their children and to improvise freely in devising similar experiences for the areas illustrated as well as for other areas.

Throughout the bulletin the keynote is "Help children develop a 'feel' for the forces around them, learn to do straight thinking about them, and develop a social conscience with respect to them."

ALICE MIEL

Preface

THERE is great concern in this and other countries lest the young people best suited to advance the fields of science and technology choose other areas of specialization. It is important that such talent not be wasted. But in a democracy it is equally important that we have an informed general population. We need adults, regardless of how they make their living, who will read, listen, think, and then use their understanding to help work toward the solution of local, national, and international problems. There is much in the content of science which can contribute toward the development of individuals who can live adequately today as well as tomorrow.

Children are curious about their environment, and under the leadership of interested teachers and other adults they can explore many natural phenomena. All children need an opportunity to deal with scientific phenomena. Some, because of interest and ability, will make great progress; but all will profit, each in his own way, by numerous and varied experiences in the different areas of science.

This book has been written with the hope that it will help teachers to provide science experiences for boys and girls and to interpret the effectiveness of such experiences in the development of concepts—concepts to be evaluated in terms of changes in behavior. There has been an honest effort to give specific suggestions and yet to provide guidance and stimulation to teachers for the development of their individual and independent ways of working with children.

Chapter One gives definite help to classroom teachers who are interested in using science experiences in helping children to grow. It presents a point of view and a program practical for classroom teachers and consistent with good science teaching in the elementary school. It helps teachers to see how some of their own concepts in the areas of time, space, change, adaptation, interrelationships, variety, and energy might have been developed. This background is used to show how teachers can help children have experiences which will cause them to revise old concepts and build new ones in each of these areas.

Chapter Two will help teachers in planning and evaluating science experiences to foster various kinds of growth. Chapter Three presents a point of view about science equipment. It also includes suggestions for caring for equipment. Chapters Four and Five give specific suggestions for experiences which will help children participate in the exploration of the world about them. The experiences were written with the hope that they would stimulate thinking and questioning and would not encourage the slavish following of directions. Numerous suggestions have been made to encourage teachers and children to think of ways they may modify an experience as here described. Given freedom of thought and expression, it is likely that children will propose experiences that will have great value for them as well as for their classmates.

No attempt has been made to indicate age or grade placement for the experiences. Children in different parts of the country and in different environments within the same area will have varied backgrounds. And those boys and girls in a fifth grade who have had four years of well-planned science experiences will be ready for quite different experiences from those appropriate for fifth grade boys and girls who have had few if any opportunities to explore and interpret their environment under competent direction. One of your best clues in selecting experiences is to try one or two you think suitable and develop a sensitivity to the way children react to them. If the children seem bored and already able to give good explanations of the principles involved, then different experiences are needed. Perhaps more advanced experiences in the same area or experiences in another area should be tried. Children who are free to express their ideas will indicate by their questions those areas in which they need simpler or more advanced experiences. Another clue for selecting experiences may come from watching the behavior of boys and girls. Sometimes children will not behave in the way you think they should. This is an indication that they have not had enough of the experiences which will lead to the behavior desired.

A list of equipment necessary for all of the experiences suggested in Chapters Four and Five has purposely been omitted. The reason is that no one class would be expected to have all of the experiences.

Therefore, an alphabetical list would be of little practical value. As you and your boys and girls plan your science program, you will need to give attention to the equipment you will need for the specific experiences you wish to have.

The ideas expressed in this book have grown out of my experiences with a wide variety of natural phenomena and out of an early and continued interest in materials and guidance in their care and use. My ideas have been influenced by reading and formal study in child development, psychology, methods of teaching, and many areas of science, and by my experience as a teacher of science—in an elementary school for six years, in a junior high school for four years, and in a senior high school for three years. For the past seven years I have worked with pre-service and in-service teachers in college classroom and laboratory. In all of this work, I have made a conscious effort to incorporate into my thinking and ultimately into my behavior those learnings which seemed valuable. As a result I am unable to give "the sources" of most of my understandings and beliefs. In other words, the ideas expressed in this book are an outgrowth of many experiences and are now a part of me.

I am deeply indebted to the many students, teachers, and others who have contributed much to my growth. I wish especially to thank Professors Gerald S. Craig, Margaret Lindsey, and Kenneth Wann for their encouragement and guidance; the late Professor Corrie W. Allen for her critical evaluation of much of this material and for her warm friendship and guidance during twenty years of teaching; and Professors Elizabeth Burger and Paul Williams and Miss Elizabeth Mussen for their criticism of parts of this material.

MARY SHECKLES

Danbury, Connecticut
1957

Contents

EDITOR'S INTRODUCTION	v
PREFACE	vi
One. YOU CAN TEACH SCIENCE	1
You Can Learn to Feel Adequate in Teaching Science	1
You can say, "I do not know"	1
You can learn with children	2
You can make mistakes	3
You Can Evaluate in Terms of Behavior Goals	4
You Can Build Basic Concepts	6
Concepts relating to time	7
Concepts relating to space	8
Concepts relating to change	10
Concepts relating to adaptation	11
Concepts relating to variety	12
Concepts relating to interrelationships	14
Concepts relating to energy	15
Application of concept development	18
You Can Plan Science Experiences	19
Guidelines from society	19
Guidelines from children	22
Two. PLANNING SCIENCE EXPERIENCES FOR CHILDREN	24
Planning Experiences to Influence a Specific Response	24
Planning Experiences to Help Children Solve a Current Problem of Living	27
Planning Experiences to Broaden the Horizons of Children and to Enrich Their Environment	29
Help in Evaluating Your Efforts	31

Contents

Three. EQUIPMENT—ITS SELECTION AND CARE   35

Equipment Should Be Safe   35
Equipment Should Be Simple   39
Some Special Science Equipment Is Needed   40
A Way of Sharing and Caring for Equipment Is Needed   45

Four. THE SOLID PART OF THE EARTH   48

Rocks and Minerals: Experiences   50
To look at rocks and minerals in their natural surroundings   50
To practice conservation in collecting rocks and minerals   51
To group rocks and minerals   52
    To use simple tests for hardness   52
    To identify limestone and marble   53
    To group rocks formed under similar conditions   53
To see how some sedimentary rocks might have been formed   54
    To see how shale might have been formed   55
    To see how sandstone might have been formed   55
    To examine limestone as an aid in understanding how it might have been formed   56
To see how mineral crystals might have been formed   57
    To make soda crystals   57
    To make crystals of different sizes   58
    To examine rocks and minerals for crystals   58
To record observations or interpretations of rock formations   59
    By making drawings   59
    By making sand pictures   59
    By using clay models   60
To discover what a fossil is   60
To find out where to look for fossils   61
To make impressions of leaves and shells   63
    By using mud or clay   63
    By using plaster of Paris   63
To determine the age of rocks by studying their position   63

Soils and Erosion: Experiences   64
To observe soils in one's immediate surroundings   64
To study what is in soil   65
To make a mixture as nearly like soil as possible   65
To find which soil material will hold the most water   66
To observe the movement of water in cloth   67
To observe the results of the movement of water in soil   67
To test soils for acidity or alkalinity   68
To test different samples of soil to see in which a given kind of plant will grow best   69
To look for evidence of erosion in one's surroundings   70

Contents   xi

To observe differences in eroded and non-eroded areas	71
To show that all material in an area is not weathered and eroded by water at the same rate	71
To show by experiment some of the ways in which rocks are weathered	72
By friction	72
By freezing water	73
By rapid heating and cooling	76
By chemical action	76
To show some of the factors which help to cause rapid soil erosion	77
To compare water run-off in soil with and without grass	77
To test the effect of elevation on water erosion	78
To compare water run-off in different kinds of plantings	78
To see the effect of wind erosion in different plantings	79
To observe areas where erosion has been checked	80
To make plans for checking erosion in an area children have observed	80
Films on Rocks, Minerals, Soils, and Erosion	81

Five. THE GASEOUS AND LIQUID PARTS OF THE EARTH   83

The Gaseous Part—The Atmosphere (Air): Experiences   85

To show that air is in many places	85
To find that places where we can breathe contain air	85
To find that air is in some places that seem empty	86
To show that air is in "empty" jars	86
To show that air is in "empty" boxes	86
To show that air is in soil	87
To show that air is in water	87
To show that air is in rocks	87
To find that things which are full of air cannot be filled with something else unless the air can get out	88
To fill with water a jar that is full of air	88
To fill with water a medicine dropper full of air	88
To observe that air is lighter than water	89
To show that air can be put into some things	89
To put air into water	89
To put air into soapy water	90
To put air into a paper bag	90
To put air into a balloon, inner tube, or ball bladder	90
To transfer air from one jar into another jar	90
To practice a safe way to strike a match	91
To show that air (oxygen) is necessary for things to burn	92
To put out a fire by excluding air (oxygen)	92
To show that air contains different substances	94
To show that there is water in air	94
To cause water to come out of the air	94
To observe that water evaporates into the air	95

Contents

To make a small cloud	96
To observe that water comes out of the air	97
To decrease the oxygen in a jar of air by burning a candle in it	97
To show that when a candle burns, carbon dioxide is given off into the air	98
To show that human beings exhale carbon dioxide into the air as they breathe	98
To observe dust in the air	98
To show that plant spores may be in the air	99
To observe that moving air has great force and can lift heavy objects	99
To show that air can be used to lift books or other weights	100
To show that air holds some things up and retards their rate of falling	100
To show that if two pieces of paper of equal size are dropped from the same height, the one with the greater surface exposed to the air will fall more slowly	100
To make and use a simple parachute	101
To observe balloons filled with air or gases	101
To show that air pressure is decreased in a stream of air	102
To decrease pressure over a strip of paper	102
To decrease pressure under a folded strip of paper	102
To decrease pressure between two ping pong balls	103
To show that air exerts pressure	103
To feel the pressure of air against a moving object	103
To observe the effect of the pressure of moving air against a pinwheel	104
To show that water will rise in a bottle if part of the air is forced out and the bottle inverted in a pan of water	105
To use air pressure to make a fountain in a bottle	105
To show that air pressure is necessary if one is to drink through a straw	106
To show that air pressure helps us to pour liquids out of a narrow mouth bottle or jug	106
To show that air pressure helps us to pour liquids out of a can	107
To show that air presses on a card with enough force to keep water in a tumbler	107
To show how a siphon works	108
To show that air pressure can be used to pick up small objects from the bottom of an aquarium	109
To show that suction cups work because of air pressure	110
To see the effect of a great deal of air pressure in resisting force	110
To determine the approximate amount of air pressure being exerted	111
To make a simple barometer	111
To show that when air pressure in a can is decreased, the air pressure outside the can will be great enough to cause the sides of the can to be bent in	111

Contents

To show that air pressure can be used to put a hard-cooked egg in a bottle, and also to take the egg out of the bottle	112
To observe that hot air is lighter than cold air	113
To observe that differences in temperature cause movement of air	114
To show that air expands when heated	114
To inflate a balloon by heating air in a bottle	114
To feel a balloon expand as the air in it is heated	114
To measure the expansion of the balloon	115
To show that air contracts when cooled	115
To show that hot air moves up	115
To observe that on a calm day smoke goes straight up	116
To observe that air over a hot radiator is moving up	116
To show convection currents in a jar of air	116

The Liquid Part of the Earth—Water: Experiences   117

To observe that water goes into some things and runs off of other things	119
To show that some things float in water and others do not	119
To show that things float higher in salt water than in fresh water	120
To show that water is taken up by air (evaporation)	121
To show that rate of evaporation is not always the same	121
To show that temperature affects evaporation	121
To show that moving air speeds up evaporation	121
To show that surface area affects evaporation	122
To observe that the humidity affects evaporation	122
To show the relation between evaporation, cooling, and personal comfort	123
To feel the cooling effect of rapid evaporation	123
To observe that movement of air alone does not cause cooling	123
To feel the cooling effect when movement of air is used to speed up evaporation	124
To observe the cooling effect when movement of air is used to speed up evaporation	124
To show that water may be taken out of air	125
To observe that water comes out of the air	125
To show that many things contain water	125
To become conscious that the care of public water is our responsibility	126
To observe that rivers and lakes may be contaminated	126
To show one way to clean water	127
To show that water can be stored	127
To observe that water is essential to certain types of recreation	128
To show that some things dissolve in water and that others do not	128
To show that when most water evaporates solid particles are left	129
To show that running water has great force	129
To show that water may be changed to a gas or a solid	130
To change water to steam by using heat	130

To change water to ice by taking away heat	130
To change steam to water by taking away heat	131
To change ice to water by adding heat	131
To observe that water in its gaseous form can exert great pressure	131
To observe that water in its solid form, ice, is lighter than the liquid form, water	132
To observe that water expands when it freezes	132
To observe that warm water rises	132
Films on Air and Water	133
Six. IDEAS IN REVIEW	134
BIBLIOGRAPHY	137
EQUIPMENT SUPPLY HOUSES	138

CHAPTER ONE

You Can Teach Science

You, a classroom teacher, *can* teach science. You have had many experiences in which you have dealt adequately with science phenomena. If you had not, you would not have survived on this earth long enough to become a teacher. You as a classroom teacher not only can but should be the one to teach science to the boys and girls in your class. Having specialized in working with children, you know much about the ways in which the boys and girls in your classroom think, work, and play. You need not hesitate to work with children in the area of science.

YOU CAN LEARN TO FEEL ADEQUATE IN TEACHING SCIENCE

It is not enough to be told that you can teach science. You need to develop a feeling of adequacy in working with children in this area. The material which follows is designed to help you to work constructively toward such a feeling of adequacy.

You can say "I do not know"

When working with children in unfamiliar subject matter you may say, "I do not know." This is no plea for ignorance. Our present body of information is so great that it is impossible for any individual to gain all the available knowledge. You, as an honest person, can admit that there are many things which you do not know. For example, why should you, a specialist in working with children, be expected to identify all the rocks that your pupils bring in, when specialists in the field of geology rarely identify a rock without taking it to the laboratory and making a series of tests? A frank response of "I do not know" or a tentative statement such as "It looks like sandstone, but I am not sure" may be just as useful as being able to make the direct statement, "It is sandstone." The really important thing here, when working with children, is the manner and tone of voice in which the response is given. If you say to a child, "I do not know," with a feeling of, "Go away, leave me alone. Don't ask such silly questions," then you have blocked, at least temporarily, the avenue to learning in that area. But if you say with sincerity, "I do not know," and quickly follow with, "How do you suppose we could find out? Where could we look for information?" or a similar statement, then a whole new area may be opened up for study.

You can learn with children

If you put off helping your boys and girls to have rewarding experiences in the area of science until you feel you know enough science subject matter, you will probably never start. There is much to learn; and the more you study, the more you find there is to learn. In modern science you need not apologize for, nor hesitate to admit, learning with your children. Often you will be a more helpful leader when there are new elements in a situation to present a real challenge to everyone.

You should not feel that you must teach all that is known about an area of science just because you introduce your class to the area. In fact, it would not be desirable to do so even if you could. Information about the universe, the earth, and living and non-living things on the earth is continuously being accumulated, and you will want the boys and girls in your class to be alert to new discoveries and accounts of reorganized thought. One of your goals is to help children to think logically, to observe, to reason, and to search for the best available information. You will not, therefore, want to teach with finality any area of science. Rather, you will want to leave children with the feeling that there is much more they would like to do and learn in each area of science.

Since the field of science is so great and your duties as a classroom teacher are so numerous, you may find that a child knows more about a topic than you do. Do not let this bother you. It is only natural that a child who spends every free minute working on a motor, reading about jet planes, reading about and taking care of nonpoisonous snakes, or following any other special scientific interest will come to know much. You may never have had time to learn a lot in any of these areas. It does not follow that you would not be interested in hearing Bill tell about garter snakes or seeing Joe demonstrate the motor he has made. Let a child with special interest share his information with the group. The sharing of information within the group can be a desirable and stimulating experience. You, too, may catch the enthusiasm. You do not need to feel that all information must come from you. Helping children to seek and to share knowledge is a way in which you may be of great value to them.

You can make mistakes

If you do not speak in an absolute manner or use dogmatic methods in your teaching, you can admit being wrong. It is very difficult to make absolute statements all day and have all of them entirely correct. You will be setting a far more realistic pattern for your boys and girls to follow if, when in doubt about your information, you preface a statement by a phrase such as "I think," "I believe," or "so far as I know." In science you should try always to give the most accurate information you have. At the same time you will need to be aware that there may be new information which you have not yet had an opportunity to evaluate. Accuracy is something you will always work for, but it is not a static goal that you can reach.

In a discussion you may find that a child is right and you are wrong. That, too, is all right. The situation should not disturb you unless you have been dogmatic. Such an experience should help children learn to evaluate a statement rather than the person who made the statement. In science it is not a question of who is right but of what is right. Children should be encouraged to evaluate statements. If a statement is made which differs from that which a child can accept, then he needs to ask questions and to find out more about the evidence on which the statement is based. After considering the new information, he may wish to change his ideas. Or he may reject the new and cling to his original idea. How a person reacts to challenge and to new information is a significant part of his behavior pattern.

It is important in science to give the source of your information. You cannot discover for yourself every bit of information you need to know. You are dependent on the heritage of the race as well as on those who are adding to present-day information. Children should also be encouraged to give the sources of their statements. For example, you or a student may preface an account with a remark similar to one of the following: "Last Saturday when I was in Jim's back yard, I noticed . . . ," "I read in Ditmar's book *Reptiles of the World* that . . . ," "I heard on the radio this morning that . . . ," "Last night on television, I saw . . . ," or "My father told me . . ."

YOU CAN EVALUATE IN TERMS OF BEHAVIOR GOALS

You may wish to think a little about goals before you accept the idea that you can teach science. What will you be trying to do as you teach science? The general goal of science in childhood education is to contribute in as many ways as possible to the growth and development of boys and girls, helping them to become well-balanced, poised, resourceful individuals with the ability to think logically, to determine the degree to which a statement is based on fact or fiction, and to live with adequacy in whatever type of environment they find themselves. Science is by no means the only subject matter area which contributes to this goal, but experiences in science can contribute much toward its achievement.

The point, somewhat more simply stated, is that you will be working for changes in the behavior of your boys and girls which will make them the best possible citizens in our democracy. This means that you will need to look for indications of beginning change and for actual changes in the behavior of your pupils. What do John, Sue, Martha, and all the rest do differently as a result of their work with you in science? In judging the success of your science program, you will no longer be dependent on how glibly your pupils respond orally or in writing, but will use observation of behavior as a valuable part of evaluation.

As you start your science work, try not to expect perfection in yourself or in your children. Learn to look for evidences in yourself and in your boys and girls of growth toward behavior that is desirable in our democracy. The following are a few indications of growth which may help you get started with your observations. The degree to which any of these can be expected will be dependent on the age, past experiences, and maturity of the children in your group. As you work with your group you may wish to revise some of these statements, add your own examples, and add new statements.

1. Do children search for explanations of natural events? That is, are they not only curious but interested in finding explanations of the things they observe?

2. Do children use their present information as a basis for logical thinking about their observations? Their explanations may be incorrect but should be recognized as attempts to do good thinking.

3. Do children question explanations based on magic and superstition? Are they willing to try to find logical explanations for the phenomena in question?

4. Do children look for more than one source of information?

5. Do children begin to question and make some choice between sources of information?

6. Do children attempt to distinguish between fact and fiction? This is sometimes difficult when one is unfamiliar with the phenomenon being discussed.

7. Do children label the source of their information?

8. Do children challenge the explanations made by others and accept challenge of their own explanations in a wholesome manner?

9. Do children change their ideas when new evidence is presented?

10. Do children repeat experiments to check whether or not they get the same results each time?

11. Do children check their conclusions with authoritative sources? When such sources are written materials, children who do not read well may have difficulty. The experience, however, may serve as a stimulus to a child who has felt no need to read.

12. Do children show growth in the manipulation of materials?

13. Do children give evidence of growth in resourcefulness? That is, if the materials called for in the directions for an experiment are not available, are they able to suggest and use substitutes? Do they make suggestions of ways to find out information? Can they plan and carry out an experiment to demonstrate a point in question?

14. Do children show an awareness of the value of materials? That is, do they use and store tools, brushes, paints, books, and other materials properly after learning the correct care of such materials? Do they save and use scrap materials?

15. Do children voluntarily show a feeling of responsibility for their environment? For example, does Bill voluntarily put waste materials in the nearest container for waste rather than throwing them down on the school ground, street, picnic area, or wherever he happens to be? Are children better "housekeepers" in their classroom? Do they walk on sidewalks and designated paths rather than across grass and flower beds?

16. Do children show an awareness of the needs of living things both in their planning and in their care of living things in the classroom?

Such changes in the behavior of your boys and girls as those suggested above may occur slowly. In fact, the changes you are working for may not occur during the year but may occur later. Individuals, regardless of age, do not change their behavior patterns easily or quickly. But desirable changes in behavior are worth working and waiting for. Do not be easily discouraged. And do not expect all children to progress at the same rate or as far and as rapidly as you might like. Desirable changes in behavior, however, will remain a part of your boys and girls long after they have forgotten much of the subject matter they verbalized under your guidance.

YOU CAN BUILD BASIC CONCEPTS

Let us now look for a way to organize some of the great body of science information which you already have and which you will continue to augment. Some who have given a great deal of thought to this problem have developed what might be called six large or basic science patterns.[1] These patterns appear to be universal, in that they apply in all nations and in rural and urban cultures. The basic science patterns have been called time, space, change, adaptation, variety, and interrelationships. There is another large pattern which seems to fit in this group. This is the pattern of energy. Evidences of energy may be found throughout the universe and have been present in the universe since its beginning. Thus it would seem that it might be included as the

---

[1] Gerald S. Craig, *Science for the Elementary-School Teacher* (Boston: Ginn and Company, 1947), pp. 11-12; National Society for the Study of Education, Forty-sixth Yearbook, Part I, *Science Education in American Schools*, Section II (Chicago: The University of Chicago Press, 1947), pp. 60-105.

seventh large basic pattern of science. As we live we develop concepts related to each of these large patterns.

Concepts are not new to you, for you have been developing them ever since you started reacting to your environment. Concepts are ideas or generalized thoughts which you have concerning the different phenomena you deal with throughout life. You have many, many concepts. Some are conscious and well developed because of rich experiences, and others remain almost dormant. You are continuously reorganizing some of your old concepts and adding new ones.

Concepts govern what you do. You may never have had an occasion to verbalize many of these, but your behavior is an indication of what your concepts are. You have concepts which direct your behavior in religious matters, business transactions, recreation, social contacts, and all of your other activities; but for the purpose of the present discussion let us consider the seven universal patterns which deal more specifically with science phenomena. In reality these are not set apart in you where they can be called into action only when teaching science or dealing with phenomena related to science, nor do your concepts relating to these basic patterns develop independently of other concepts. All of your concepts are integrated into a behavior pattern which in effect controls what you do. However, each of the seven basic science patterns just mentioned has been dealt with separately, in the discussion which follows, in an attempt to indicate what may have been some of the experiences which greatly influenced the development of your own concepts.

Concepts relating to time

If someone should ask you to state your concepts of time, there might be quite a long pause before you began to talk. Yet you have many concepts concerning time, some developed in earliest childhood and others acquired through many later experiences. Do you remember in those early years how long it was before "next weekend"? And how unbearably long it was between one birthday and the next? How rapidly they occur now! A study of history and literature helped you to place people and events into a time sequence. When you studied rocks and the age of the earth, you gained new ideas to incorporate into your expanding concepts of time. Perhaps a drive through the giant redwood forests in California impressed you with the age of some of those beautiful trees. Or maybe as you stood at the rim of the Grand Canyon of the Colorado River you wondered about the age of the rocks in those great walls. Then you read or heard the ranger tell of the age of the canyon and how it was formed. Perhaps you traveled through other parts of the world and saw evidences of ancient civilizations. Or maybe you saw pictures and heard someone else tell of his travels in faraway places. All of these experiences and many more have gone into the building of your concepts of time.

If you have had this kind of rich experience, then you are aware that the earth is very old. You may also be aware that some rocks are older than others and that the basic material of soil comes from rock. All of this should have a great effect on your behavior. You will probably be concerned about the erosion of soil, for you realize the great length of time necessary to change solid rock into the basic material of good soil. You will actively work to check erosion on your own property and be of whatever service you can in preventing erosion of other land. You will be concerned about forest fires, for you realize their great destruction to living things and to the soil, and you will have some understanding of the great length of time it takes for the land to become productive again. If you smoke, you will be very careful with matches and lighted cigarettes. You will be interested in voting for legislation which will provide adequate fire-detecting and fire-fighting service for our nation's forests. In fact, your outlook on the wise use of our natural resources will be influenced to a great degree by your concepts of time. If you conceive of our resources as being built up rapidly, you will behave quite differently from the way you will act if you realize the enormous length of time which was required for their formation. Even our great synthetics industry has not freed us from dependence on natural resources that were built up in the course of many centuries and that cannot be replaced in a few years or even in a few lifetimes. Your concepts of time influence the way you think about our exhaustible resources.

Concepts relating to space

Have you become quite space-conscious in recent years? Maybe the building and launching of satellites which revolve about the earth has recently sharpened your interest. Perhaps you have visited one of the many astronomical observatories and looked through a telescope at some of the sights of the universe—stars, planets, comets, moons, and galaxies. Whatever recent stimuli there may be, some of your concepts of space started at an early age. The early explorations of your bed and bedroom and your later adventures into the other rooms in the house, the yard, and the house next door all helped you to develop concepts of space. Later there were trips to town, neighboring towns, other states, and perhaps international travels.

Did you climb trees, and fences, or maybe play in a hayloft or on a barn roof when you were a child? If so, did you ever fall? Both the going up and the coming down, accidental or otherwise, added new experiences in space travel for you. Swinging, and sliding down banisters, hillsides, or playground slides, also gave you new sensations in relation to the ground and the atmosphere.

As you watched clouds you may have become aware that some are close to the ground and others are far away. Perhaps watching clouds move and smoke rise from chimneys or industrial stacks gave you some feeling about the space above you.

In school you studied maps and learned to locate the continents and oceans. You read about and saw pictures of people and places in different parts of the world. Perhaps there was a globe to represent the earth and you learned what causes day and night and seasonal change. You began to read about how far away the moon, the planets, the sun and other stars are from the earth. Can you recall when you learned that the sun is larger than your room, your school, and even the earth? When you could stay up late at night, you probably looked at the stars and talked about how far away they were. Perhaps you saw meteors and wondered from how far out in space they came.

If you have traveled by plane, you have had a different look at the earth and space. You have seen how familiar objects appear smaller and smaller as you fly at greater heights. This helps with your understanding of how the sun can be so large and yet appear so small. You had gained some idea of this while traveling on the ground, of course. But the experience from the air also helps. Flying through and above the clouds also adds to your feeling for objects out in space.

You have probably had many more experiences which have contributed to your concepts of space. Are you interested in space travel? Would you like to go to the moon? Can you enjoy seeing a meteor streak across the sky? Do you like to read about cosmic rays and magnetic storms on the sun? Are you fascinated by auroral displays? Your answers to these and similar questions would reveal much about your concepts of space.

Concepts relating to change

Changes have been going on around you all of your life. Your concepts of change have resulted from your awareness of some of these. The changes in temperature, pressure, light, surrounding medium, and other conditions which you experienced at birth started you on your separate existence in an environment of change.

Not long after birth you began to experience the changes from light to darkness and back to light again. Experiences with changes in clothing began early. It probably was not long before you responded to changes in the tone of voice of your mother and others who took care of you. Changes in the weather were also part of your early experiences.

As you grew there were changes in your body proportions and muscle development. With these came changes in the work you could do. There were also changes in the kinds of activities which gave you pleasure. Changes occurred in the kinds of food you could eat. And your likes and dislikes concerning food have not remained the same. With growing up you experienced changes in the kind of help your mother gave you. In school your first grade teacher gave you help quite different from that which you received from your sixth grade teacher.

Perhaps not long after you became interested in plants and animals you began to notice some changes in them. Changes in the color of leaves and the dropping of leaves in the fall may have been among your early observations of plants. You may have lived where you could watch the coats of some animals change color with a change in season. Perhaps you became aware that birds lose many of their feathers at a certain time of the year.

There were also changes in the appearance of people. Sometimes a person might be happy and smiling and at other times worried and glum. As years went by, you probably noticed that some of your older friends developed wrinkles in their faces and that their hair became gray. Some of the men you saw lost much of their hair and became bald.

In school perhaps you learned how certain chemicals change when they are heated. Or you learned how chemical energy in a dry cell can be changed into electrical energy which in turn may become light or heat energy.

Your experiences with change have given you certain concepts about change. Many of these are evident in your behavior. For example, you buy clothing suitable for wear in the different seasons because you confidently expect change in the weather. You plan certain activities based on your concepts of changes which occur in the weather and day and night. You know that heat causes desirable changes in certain foods; therefore, in preparing meals you plan to cook certain foods. The behavior pattern resulting in the regular saving of a part of your earnings may result from the realization of changes which come with age.

Concepts relating to adaptation

You react to living things in certain ways because of your concepts relating to their adaptation to their environment. You probably observed the results of adaptation long before you became aware of the word. These early observations were a beginning for the development of concepts. That is, in the fall of the year you noticed and perhaps played with pretty tree leaves which you found on the ground. It may have been several years later that you began to know that trees lose much moisture through their leaves, and that for many trees leaf fall is an adaptation for survival during a period of limited liquid water.

If you had a pet dog, you may have noticed that each year its fur became thicker before cold weather. You may not at first have thought of this as an adaptation for protection against the cold. Maybe you had a pet turtle that hibernated during the winter months. (Perhaps you learned that *hibernate* is from the Latin word for *winter*.) As you heard about or observed other animals that hibernate in the winter, you may have developed the concept that some animals survive cold winters by hibernating. If you lived in or near a hot desert region, you may have observed that some of the animals estivate during the driest season. (You may be learning just now that *estivate* is from the Latin word for *summer*.) This, too, you may have recognized as an adaptation for survival.

You may have observed rather early that the mouths of animals are different. You probably noticed that animals do not all eat the same kinds of food. But it might not have been until you were older that you made the association between the structure of an animal's mouth and the kind of food it eats. You developed the concept that the structure of the mouth of an animal shows an adaptation for the kind of food that animal will eat.

You reveal some of your concepts concerning the adaptation of plants and animals when you move them from one environment to another. If you have a well-developed concept of the adaptation of a plant for survival in its natural habitat, you will not transplant it into an entirely different habitat. Instead, if it is growing in a moist, shady place, you will transfer it to a similar habitat.

You also show your awareness that great numbers of offspring are an adaptation for survival of house flies when you make the extra effort to kill the first few flies you see in the spring. This same concept will prompt you to cut unwanted seed plants before they produce mature seed.

Concepts relating to variety

At birth you became dependent on different people. There was great variation in the appearance of these people, in the sound of their voices, in their reactions to you, and in your reactions to them. They varied in age, height, weight, complexion, the way they dressed, and kind of disposition. They did a variety of things for you. Throughout your life you have continued to meet and to know many people, no two of whom were ever exactly alike.

Probably rather early in life you became aware of the great variety of non-living things around you. The objects in your room and even in your bed were not all alike. There were toys of different shapes, sizes, colors, and kinds of material. You played with them in different ways. Some objects you came in contact with were hard, others soft; some were smooth, others rough; some were hot, others cold; some moved, and others did not move.

You may have learned to associate movement with living things. As your experiences with living things became greater, you probably found some were friendly and others hostile. Later you found out that some living things, like trees and most other plants, do not move around. Then you developed new concepts to help you distinguish between living and non-living objects.

As you grew you learned to use a wide variety of materials. For example, you found out that newspapers were read and soon discarded. Books were also read but they were not thrown away. You may have noticed a difference in the kind of paper that is used for newspapers and for books. You learned that certain kinds of paper are to write on, others are for drawing and making things, and still other kinds are for wrapping food, clothing, or gifts.

Perhaps you had experiences with different kinds of wood. The furniture in the living room may have been made of a different kind of wood from that in your bedroom. The wood that was burned in the fireplace was different from that which you worked on in shop. You may have discovered that some woods are soft and others hard, and that they vary in color. Some are dark like ebony and black walnut, while others are light, like white pine and maple.

Can you remember your first shopping trip? What a variety of things there were to buy! How hard it was to make decisions when there were so many different kinds of things from which to choose!

Perhaps you became aware of differences in sands and soils. Beach sand was not like river sand. And if you visited several beaches you may have found that the sand was not alike on all beaches. Some may have been fine and some coarse. It probably varied in color. You may also have found out that river sand is not all alike. The soil in your back yard may have been different from that in your grandparents' yard. And both might look quite different from that which you saw in a plowed field.

You may have observed that different kinds of plants and animals lived in different places. Perhaps there were doodle-bug holes in the loose soil under the back steps. Even these varied in size. Maybe there were horned toads that lived in your grandparents' yard. Was there an old toad that stayed in a damp, cool place during the hot day and came hopping out in the later afternoon and fed on insects? There were probably many kinds of animals both large and small that you learned to know. Each was different from all the rest.

Plants, too, were of many kinds. Some were large like the old live oak tree down on the corner. And some were small like the mosses growing in the shade near the bank of a stream. Some were green like ferns and others were a light cream color like some mushrooms.

You can fill in many more experiences which you have had that **made you aware of difference in living and non-living things.** You are surrounded by things which are different, yet your behavior may indicate that you have not made the concepts concerning variety a part of your conscious actions. The concepts related to variety are one of the foundations on which we build human relationships. According to your concepts of variety you will be able to accept or reject wide variations in the people with whom you work. Such concepts will also partly determine how you accept or reject variations within yourself. If you have well-developed concepts in this area, you will not expect other people to think as you do on all matters, or to have the same likes and dislikes that you have. If you move to a different part of the country, you will expect people, plants, animals, climate, soil, rock formations, and everything else to be different in some ways from those to which you have been accustomed.

Concepts relating to interrelationships

You have been interacting with your environment since birth. And you will continue to interact with it as long as you live. The altitude, temperature, and humidity all affect you. Even as an infant you reacted to changes in these, although you may not have been conscious of these reactions until several years later.

Interrelationships with people started early for you. Your first means of communication was that of crying. You had different cries for different occasions. Your mother soon learned whether you cried from hunger, pain, or fright. As you grew and developed other means of communication, crying frequently brought punishment. Also with age came contacts with more people. Sometimes your interactions with people were favorable and at other times unfavorable. But always you interacted with people.

Perhaps in school you experimented with plants. If so, you found that they reacted to light. Perhaps you also found that there was a relationship between the growth of plants and the kind of soil in which they were growing. Buds which form on trees during the spring and summer gave you an opportunity to see the relation between buds and seasons.

If you had pets, you had a chance to see how dependent they were on you for their food, water, and care. And you probably became dependent on them for their loyalty and responsiveness to you. Maybe you learned about some of the specific plants and animals that are interdependent. If you lived in dry regions where yucca plants grow, you may have learned how dependent they are on the yucca moth for pollination, and how the moth in turn is dependent on the yucca for a place to lay its eggs. Maybe you observed honeybees visiting flowers and became aware that the bees not only took nectar but also took pollen. Some of the pollen they used, and some was transferred to other blossoms.

Did you ever see aphids on a plant and on close inspection find that there were several ants around as guards? This is an interrelationship in which the ants protect and care for the aphids. The aphids suck plant juices and give these to the ants. Maybe you have read about or seen crabs with sponges or anemones on their shells. The crabs gain protection and the sponges or anemones profit by being carried about to different feeding areas.

If you have read accounts of animals and plants becoming extinct, you may realize how much the activities of men are interrelated with those of other living things. News reports of floods and discussions about ways to prevent or lessen the damage may have given you an entirely new feeling concerning the interrelationships between men and the natural forces.

The experiences which have contributed to your present concepts concerning interrelationships have no doubt been varied and numerous. Your present behavior shows how you have reacted to some of these experiences. What is your attitude toward killing harmless snakes, draining all swamps, building power dams without any consideration of the total complex of interrelationships involved in such construction? Do you throw trash from your automobile windows, litter a picnic area, break branches off flowering trees such as redbud and dogwood, pull up flowers by their roots, and bring in whole branches of beautiful leaves in the fall? Your behavior in the out-of-doors and your ways of working with others tell much about your concepts of interrelationships.

Concepts relating to energy

You began your use of energy before birth and will continue to use energy as long as you live. Not long after birth you were given milk to drink. This became a new source of energy for you as you began to live in the atmosphere. Your body used this milk to grow and to move. As you grew you were given other kinds of foods. These, too, supplied your body with energy. Food is the source of your energy supply now, just as it was when you were an infant.

You began to experience different forms of energy at an early age. Light energy was new to you at birth. You continued to observe and to use light energy as you grew. Unless you have lost your sight, you are dependent on light energy to help you find your way both indoors and out-of-doors. In fact almost everything you do except sleep requires some light energy.

Heat is also a form of energy with which you became acquainted early in life. You were probably taken out-of-doors on sunny days before you learned to crawl and to walk. If so, you experienced heat energy which came direct from the sun. On cold days you probably experienced heat which came from the burning of coal, oil, or other fuel. When you began to move about using only your own muscle energy, probably you were cautioned as you came near a hot stove. At this time you probably began to associate the words *heat* and *hot* with the sensation of warmth you had often felt. It may not have been long before you learned to associate burning with heat. You learned that matches, candles, wood, coal, and other materials gave off heat as they burned. You did not think of this heat as a form of energy but you learned to use this energy. If you lived where the winters are cold, you learned at an early age to go closer to a stove or radiator when you were cold and to move back as you became warm. You probably used or watched heat energy being used to toast bread and to cook foods. You may have seen or read about a battery, stove, or water heating system which made use of heat energy direct from the sun. Your many experiences with heat energy have given you both varied and numerous concepts in this area.

Sound is also a form of energy with which you have had experiences since birth. The sound of human voices, sounds made by animals, sounds of machines of different kinds, musical sounds, and sounds of nature such as thunder, wind, and waves as they break against the shore are some of the many kinds of sounds you have learned to recognize. You now have concepts which help you to recognize and to make use of sound energy.

The energy of wind you experienced before you knew words to express what you observed. The swaying of tree branches or the flutter of leaves, the blowing of skirts or of hats were all early observations of the evidence of the energy of moving air. When you were old enough to run and play, you may have felt the sting of sand or dirt blown against your face and legs by the wind. In some parts of the world wind is used to pump water, grind grain, or charge small home electric generating units. You may have observed these or other uses of the energy of wind. If you lived near a lake or other body of water, you may have used the energy of wind rather than your muscle energy and oars to move a boat.

There are other forms of energy with which you may have had fewer direct experiences. Perhaps you have read about or visited a dam where the energy of falling water was being used to turn large generators which produced electrical energy. Such experiences helped you to expand your concepts relating to energy. As you learned that automobiles had to have gasoline in order to run and that, if the oil or coal supply ran out, the furnace could no longer give off heat, your understandings of energy in relation to fuels became greater.

Among your more recent concepts related to energy are those which deal with atomic energy. Perhaps it came as a surprise to you to find that some scientists who have studied the sun carefully think that the enormous amount of energy released on the sun is the result of the fusion of the nuclei of hydrogen atoms. Scientists who deal with this form of energy tell us that the nucleus, the central portion of an atom, is the part that is split, as in uranium, or fused, as in hydrogen. But for those of us not working directly with this form of energy, reading such a detail makes little difference in our behavior. Those working with energy from atoms, however, use such information in planning and carrying on their work. In other words their behavior is affected.

As you have developed concepts relating to energy, your behavior has become more or less consistent with those concepts. And as you have reorganized old concepts and added new ones your behavior has changed. For example, as an adult your behavior relative to the energy released from static electricity in the form of lightning may be quite different from your reaction to lightning at the age of two. On the other hand, your behavior may still be much the same as it was when you were a child. In the latter case your concepts concerning lightning are much the same now as they were when you were a child.

As your concepts relating to the constructive uses of the energy from the nuclei of atoms develop, your behavior will change from that which you had when your concepts dealt only with the destructive use of such energy.

Application of concept development

Of course you have not had all of the experiences which have been suggested. But you have had many more of equal or greater value. Your concepts are unlike those of any other person, for no one else has had exactly your experiences. No one else has reacted to experiences in exactly the same way you have.

Not only are your concepts different from those of other people, but your concepts will not all be the same today as they were yesterday, last week, or a year ago, nor will they be the same next week or next year as they are today. Your concepts are frequently in a state of revision. And you continue to add new ones. This has been true from the time you first reacted to your environment and will remain true until you no longer react to stimuli.

Are there areas in which you feel your experiences have been limited? Perhaps by being conscious of these you can plan experiences for yourself which will help to develop broader concepts in a given area. You may also wish to plan for further development in areas in which you are already strong.

An awareness of concepts and how they may be developed is most important if you are to plan meaningful science experiences for boys and girls. Many of your children will have had experiences similar in some ways to those you had as a child. Therefore, exploring the growth of some of your own concepts should be of value in helping you get started. You will also need to take into consideration the environment of your children when making plans. Your boys and girls may be living in an environment quite unlike yours although you live in the same part of town.

By carefully observing children's behavior you will gain some clues concerning the attitudes and values developed from the concepts which they hold. If their experiences in an area are both numerous and varied, action may be very constructive. But if their experiences have been limited in an area, action in that area may be inadequate and unconstructive. Where deficiencies are discovered they may be used as guidelines in your planning. You will find few if any children who wish to be antisocial or destructive. But you will find many children of elementary school age who have never had the right experiences to enable them to be otherwise. Your sensitivity and careful planning will help them to develop many useful concepts.

YOU CAN PLAN SCIENCE EXPERIENCES

As a teacher, you have a right to plan many science experiences for your boys and girls. You may wish, however, not to plan a detailed program at the beginning of the year. It may fit in with your ways of working with children to make broad, flexible plans. For example, from past experiences with children in the same age group as your present class, you may feel that experiences with atmosphere and weather, living things, electricity, and the solid part of the earth should be the basis of your science program for the year. Or you may decide to explore light, sound, weather, machines, and living things. Perhaps there will be other areas you wish to help your children explore. But just when or how you will begin in any of these areas will be determined by your awareness of the needs and interests of your group.

The areas you plan to work in are quite large. There is much material available in each. How will you decide what experiences to draw from each area? The answer to this will come from society and from your group.

Guidelines from society

When we look at society for guidelines, what do we see? Each of us sees something different because of our individual backgrounds of experiences. We see and interpret what we see in slightly different ways. But most people in our democracy will agree that citizens with certain characteristics are needed. Perhaps not all would state these characteristics in exactly the same words, but there would probably be remarkable agreement on the basic ideas expressed. If our society is to continue to grow and remain strong we need citizens who are . . .

. . . critical-minded and free from gullibility;

. . . willing to listen to all sides of a question before making decisions;

... willing to look for new information and change their opinions if the evidence provided by the new information indicates that a change is desirable;

... capable of establishing values for themselves and willing to support these values even when to do so is unpopular;

... able to develop a high degree of sensitivity to and concern for the needs and interests of all human beings and the environment in which they live.

How can these characteristics serve as guidelines in the selection of experiences for children? If we want children to develop into adults who are critical-minded and free from gullibility they must be given many experiences that will contribute to this goal. You can provide a small part of the great number of experiences that will be needed. For example, you can give children experiences with many and varied resource materials. When they find that the pieces of information contained in different source materials do not agree, you will be able to help them learn to evaluate materials critically. If they are using printed material, you may help them learn to check for such things as recency of copyright and experience of the author. With the changes being made in many bodies of science subject matter, it is important that the newest available information be considered. And with the wealth of printed material that is now being published, it is helpful to consider the background preparation and experience of the writer. In general, when there is a difference in content, that from an author with wide experience in the field of study is most likely to be correct. Usually material from a source nearest the experience is most likely to be correct. For example, an account of an experiment showing seasonal change written by someone who has never performed the experiment but only read about it is not likely to be as accurate as an account written by a person who has performed the experiment many times. We should help children not to be too dogmatic in their acceptance of material from a person called an authority, however. Sometimes those not considered as authorities may have the most recent or the most accurate information.

If a film or other visual type of instructional material is being used, help the children to question whether the pictures are of real and natural situations or the product of someone's imagination and photographic technique. As children read advertisements or listen to them on radio and television, they should be encouraged to think critically about what is being said. For example, if one hears about a new dentifrice that will remove stain from the teeth, what might he want to learn before using the product? How it was tested, what chemicals it contains, whether it will harm the teeth, and what his dentist thinks about the product are a few of the things he may wish to find out about the new dentifrice.

When children read or hear something which is inconsistent with what they now believe, they should be encouraged to look for additional information on the topic. For example, children often have difficulty accepting the classification which lists human beings as animals. Rather than giving this as a fact which children memorize, you can provide them with experiences in observing living things. Children can be helped to see the characteristics which human beings have that make them animals. In this way you will encourage children to question rather than accept blindly what they hear, see, or read. Being conscious of this as an objective, you will be able to plan many experiences which help children to become questioning, thinking, learning adults.

You can help children learn to listen to all sides of a question before making decisions by having class discussions in an atmosphere where one can express ideas and ask questions without fear of personal criticism. Through the use of a variety of resource materials you may also help children learn to be open-minded. They can learn to form generalizations only after adequate evidence has been critically examined. Both class discussions and the use of resource materials will provide children with opportunities for finding new information. If not hurried they can learn to examine their present concepts and make any needed changes or add new concepts. You can help children in this process by creating an atmosphere where they are free to make mistakes and to admit they have changed their minds. One way of doing this is by being willing to admit your own mistakes and, in light of new information, to modify or change your thinking.

The establishment of values may be a very slow process. But it is such a vital one that it is worth all the time and effort it requires. Children must of necessity live with the basic values on which the adult society is built. But as soon as possible they need experiences which will help them to feel that these are values by which they can live. Experiences in being critical-minded and open-minded will also help in the development of values. In addition to this you can provide experiences in which children look at the values held by different people. They can explore some of the reasons for these different values. And they can examine the differences in behavior which result from these values. For example, children might discuss the desirability of killing rats. Whether we kill rats or not depends on what we know about the habits of rats and the values we hold concerning men. Children can be encouraged to find all the information they can about rats. Experiences in which rats are useful as well as those in which rats are harmful should be had. Such questions as these may be discussed: Are all rats harmful to men? In what ways are rats harmful? Do rats serve a useful purpose in their natural habitat? Should all rats be killed and thus the species be exterminated? If the children are free to develop their own values in such studies, they will have gained much more than information about rats.

The study of a problem like that of rats may also be used in helping children to develop a sensitivity to and a concern for individuals. Many experiences will be needed in order to help children be concerned about all living things. And along with these experiences others will be needed that will help children in our culture to develop values that put the health and safety of human beings above the needs of other forms of life.

Does this help you begin to see how the science experiences you provide children with may be selected, at least in part, with the needs of a citizen in our society in mind? Let us now look to the children in your group for additional help in the selection of experiences.

Guidelines from children

Children continually give us guides concerning their needs. Our problem is to become sensitive enough to recognize these clues and skilled enough to know the kinds of experiences that would provide continuous and constructive growth. We can learn about the past experiences of individual children by observing them in different situations; by listening to them talk in groups of different size and in private conversations; and by examining cumulative records if such are available. By observing a child's behavior we can see the kinds of concepts which have become a part of him. Having learned something about the past experiences and present concepts of your children, you will have some idea of where to start.

Let us look at a situation which might arise in your group. In some school systems children entering junior high school must be vaccinated for smallpox. You discover from listening to some of your sixth grade boys and girls that many have an undesirable attitude toward this coming event. By encouraging your children to talk freely about vaccination, you discover that there are many misconceptions in the group and a general lack of information. Without condemning their feelings and reactions, you may ask if they would like to study what scientists have learned about smallpox and vaccinations. Such a study will give opportunity for growth in many of the characteristics needed by members of our society.

Children give us many indications of needed experiences. Time and energy will not permit us to follow all of them. But as you and your group work together you will need to remain continually alert to the children's reactions. These will be guidelines for evaluation and will also suggest directions for further work. You will find more specific help in the selection of experiences in Chapter Two.

CHAPTER TWO

Planning Science Experiences for Children

LET us now move on from the brief, general discussion on planning science experiences to more specific points in planning. The term "experience" as used in the remaining chapters includes observations as well as manipulation or experimentation. Other types of experience, such as reading, creative writing, creative art work, viewing pictures, listening to recordings, listening to one's peers or to authorities in a given area of study, and many others, are most worth-while. All of these types of experience, especially when combined, contribute to the growth of children's concepts. The numerous and varied experiences suggested in these chapters, however, will emphasize observation and manipulation.

In planning science experiences, you may design them to achieve different purposes. These might be grouped as follows:

1. Planning experiences to influence a specific response
2. Planning experiences to help children solve a current problem of living
3. Planning experiences to broaden the horizons of children and to enrich their environment

Planning experiences to influence a specific response

Perhaps you find from observing and listening to your children during a thunderstorm that several have misconceptions about lightning and thunder. You observe that some are afraid of thunder and that others are afraid of lightning. Their behavior shows a lack of un-

Planning Science Experiences

derstanding of these natural phenomena. You decide to plan some experiences with static electricity.

You may begin by helping your children to recall some of their experiences with static electricity. These might include rubbing a cat's back in the dark and seeing sparks, walking across a rug and getting a shock when metal is touched, combing hair in the dark and seeing sparks, and receiving a shock when taking off wool, nylon, or dacron clothing. Next you may suggest reading material which will explain these common experiences which children have with static electricity. A discussion may be needed to help some of the children to see the relation between the sparks seen and the crackling heard when taking off a nylon or dacron sweater and the lightning seen and the thunder heard during an electrical storm.

After the cause of lightning and thunder is pretty well understood, the group may wish to discuss safe places to be during a thunderstorm. They may also want to learn how buildings of different kinds are protected from lightning.

A study of thunder, lightning, and other forms of static electricity should help your boys and girls to add new concepts to their present concepts of time, space, change, and energy. It should also help them to reorganize some of their existing concepts in these areas. All will not take the same things from this study. But for some members of the group there should be changes in behavior.

Suppose you have been observing your children as they enter the school cafeteria and as they eat their lunches. You notice that very few wash their hands. There seems to be a great desire to hurry through lunch and get out to the playground.

You know that these children are aware that they should wash their hands before eating. In fact, for most of this group last year, handwashing before lunch was a well established pattern of behavior. You begin to think through some of the possible reasons for this change in behavior. You know that most of the children are familiar with the word "germ." But their concept of what a germ is may be poorly developed. They may know that germs make people ill, but they may not know how germs are carried about, or how they get into their bodies. Adults say germs are on dirty hands. But the children may think of how many times they have eaten with dirty hands and not become ill. Then too, Joe may observe that Bill never washes his hands before lunch and he has not been ill all year. But Sue always washes her hands before lunch and she has been ill four times this semester.

What Joe has been told and what he observes do not fit together. Perhaps there are experiences which will help him to see why his observations and what he is told are apparently contradictory. Until this occurs Joe may wash his hands because he wishes to please his mother or his teacher, but there is not likely to be any real change in his spontaneous behavior related to washing hands before eating.

There are many experiences which may help Joe and his classmates. Here are three:

1. Keep a list of the causes of illness which kept members of the class from school during the last semester. Check with school or family physician on ways the germs, if they were the cause of illness, may have been transmitted.

2. Ask the school physician or nurse to talk with the group about the ways diseases are spread. Also ask them to discuss why dirt on the hands increases the possibility that germs are present and why washing hands will not prevent all illnesses.

3. Ask the school nurse to help set up sterile agar plates. Let a child wash only one hand. Perhaps his best friend can help him to do a good job of this. Then let him place the washed hand on one agar plate and the unwashed hand on another. If you have enough agar plates, let others do this and also follow the children's suggestions for variations in procedure. Now set the plates aside in a warm, dark place for a day or two. Then compare the number of colonies of bacteria on the plates. There should be a marked difference in the bacterial growth on the plate touched by the clean hand and the one touched by the dirty hand. Not all of the colonies represent germs but one cannot tell just by looking which colonies are harmless and which are harmful. Children need the assurance that most of the bacteria on their hands and in the air are harmless to them. But they also need to realize that there is a possibility of harmful bacteria being present.

Perhaps you or the children will think of other meaningful experiences. It is not likely that any group of experiences will result in one-hundred-per-cent improvement in spontaneous hand-washing before eating. But for those who are ready for such experiences the results should be most gratifying. Their experiences will have contributed much to their concepts of the interrelationships that exist between: themselves and bacteria; dirt and bacteria; and soap, water, bacteria, and themselves. There may also have been a contribution to their concept of variety in germs and the way different people react to different bacteria. Children may also develop some new concepts in relation to the adaptations of certain plants that enable them to live in various environments.

Sometimes planned experiences do not bring about the desired changes in behavior. If this should happen, you may find the following questions helpful in examining your procedures. Were the experiences varied enough to allow for self-selection and for differences in the growth patterns of the boys and girls? Were the children personally involved in the experiences or were they spectators? Was there time for action, reflection, and repeated action? Were your expectations of immediate results too high? Might there need to be a considerable lapse of time and then a return to the area of study with more experiences?

Planning experiences to help children solve a current problem of living

Science experiences are often valuable in helping children work out a solution to one of their problems. For example, you may have a first grade group who wish to have a room flag which they can put up each morning. Learning to use a single pulley would help.

Suppose your group of young children have made a doll house in which they wish to have lights and a doorbell. They may ask an older group of children to help with their problem. This presents a real motive for learning about circuits, dry cells, switches, and electromagnets and their use in doorbells. With the young children this may be primarily on the manipulative level. But with the older children research concerning questions such as the following might grow out of the original need: What is electricity? Where does it come from? What is inside a dry cell? How can we make an electromagnet? How can the strength of an electromagnet be changed? How can electricity be changed into light?

Perhaps you have a group of children who have made a puppet theater and wish to have footlights. This might call for learning to use dry cells and miniature light sockets. Learning to wire a circuit that will give maximum light would be a very important activity, one for which there was a real need.

These and other experiences with electricity, sound, and light help to give children broader concepts of energy. For example, electrical energy from dry cells can be changed into light energy to use in their doll house or puppet theater. And electrical energy from dry cells can also be used to produce sound energy such as they use in the doorbell on their doll house. These experiences also contribute to the growth of children's concepts related to variety of forms of energy and to change as the result of the use of energy.

Suppose you have an older group of boys who are having trouble with their baseball diamond. They are assigned to the lower level of the playground. The water which flowed from the upper level during a recent heavy rain cut a miniature valley through their ball field. Their problem is how to stop such erosion. They discuss the matter with you. This gives you an opportunity to help the group learn what causes erosion and how it can be checked. You may suggest that they examine the playground and see where erosion is and is not taking place. They may also examine the neighborhood to see if there are places where erosion has started.

Perhaps from their observations the children may begin to see a relationship between erosion and soil that has no plant cover. They may wish to do some experiments in which they carry out on a small scale some of their ideas about what causes erosion. Their interest may take them into a study of soil and its importance. They may also experiment to find possible ways of checking or preventing erosion.

After a rather thorough study of their problem, the group may be able to suggest procedures which they can carry out on their playground. Or they may need to report their findings and recommendations to the principal and wait for adult help. In either case, your group of children may form a nucleus that will be able to help other groups become aware of erosion and some of the ways it can be checked or prevented. They may invite others to see their experiments. They may keep a bulletin board which will show the progress of their study and their future plans.

The study of erosion and its correction will contribute much to children's concepts of the interrelationships between the physical forces of wind and water and soil and between all of these and people. They may become more keenly aware of the great energy of moving air and water. Change, time, and space relations in the area where erosion is occurring may also be an important part of this study. The adaptations of different varieties of grass may be studied before making recommendations for re-sodding the area. From these brief statements do you begin to see how the large patterns of the universe may be used to form a skeleton or basic structure on which to build experiences for children?

Planning experiences to broaden the horizons of children and to enrich their environment

The experiences mentioned above are only a few of the many possibilities for using science in working through vital problems of living. But suppose problems do not arise which call for experiences in an area of science you would like your children to explore. What then?

One of your responsibilities as a teacher is to open up new areas for children to explore. You do this in language arts, social studies and social learnings, number relationships, art, music, and play. You will also want to plan science experiences which will allow individuals or groups of children to learn new and interesting things about the world they live in.

For example, you may be working with children who live in a large city where they have had little contact with animals. You may wish to plan for some animal visitors. Perhaps you can have a setting hen. Or you may be able to get a small incubator and let the children have a part in caring for the eggs during incubation. It may be that you cannot have either of these but can perhaps arrange to have several baby chicks visit your class for a short time. You may have a rabbit, guinea pig, turtle, fish, snails, newt, frog, or any other small animal in your classroom for a visit. Some of these you may wish to keep for only a half-hour. Others may visit for a day or two or for longer periods of time. Guided by the age of your group or the interest of individuals, you may plan for different outcomes from the study of animals. For some children, learning how to hold and talk to an animal may be important. For others, learning to give necessary care to another living thing may be a vital need. Knowing that the health and perhaps the life of an animal depends on him may give a child a needed feeling of importance and individual worth. Some children may be interested in observing different animals. Noticing the differences in appearance, size, body covering, movement, and eating habits of animals will help to develop the concept that there is great variation among animals.

Do you have some children who bring to school a great variety of objects, both living and non-living, from the environment? If so, when a child shows you his possession, you probably react with interest and praise, for you have been taught that to act otherwise would not be good for the child. You want to continue to give praise, but you also want to plan experiences that will help the children to develop a feeling that they are responsible for their environment.

Perhaps you can begin by helping children to enjoy the observation of both living and non-living things in their natural environment and by encouraging them to share their observations with others. Then you can give praise for good observation, reporting, and behavior. This will do much to help a child build a good feeling about himself and to increase his sensitivity to and concern for his environment.

Sometimes the purpose of your group cannot be satisfied by observation in the natural habitat. Then your problem becomes one of helping them learn to evaluate a situation and to determine for themselves whether their purpose justifies taking an object from the environment. They will need to consider what the removal of the object does to the object itself and what it does to the environment.

For example, if an animal is desired, a child might need to ask himself the following questions. Will collecting hurt or kill it? Can I provide a place indoors where there will be the correct amount of light, heat, food, and water? Can I secure a cage that will protect it from its enemies and prevent its escape? Can I provide it with enough space for exercise? Will I take the responsibility of caring for the animal's needs? If these questions can be answered satisfactorily, then what changes might be caused by the removal of the animal from the environment?

When thinking about what the removal of living things does to the environment, children need to become conscious that different procedures need to be followed when a kind of living thing is plentiful and when it is scarce. For example, if there are many frogs in a pond, taking several may cause no great change in the environment. Or if there are many ferns in an area, it is not likely to change the environment greatly if two or three are taken. If three ferns are to be collected, it would be

Planning Science Experiences

desirable to help children see why they should be taken from three different places. This procedure makes it possible for new plants to grow rather quickly in the three small disturbed areas surrounded by living plants. However, in order to keep the soil from being washed away before the new plants can grow, the bare soil should be covered with twigs, leaves, or other material.

What should be done if living things of the kind desired are not plentiful in the environment? Then children should be helped to consider whether the removal of a few will cause the species to die out in that particular region. If the species should die out, what will be the effect upon the other living things in that environment? Although loss of a species in a region would not usually mean extinction of the species, you may wish to help your children gain a better understanding of just what extinction of a species means. The desirability of causing the extinction of any living species is seriously questioned, for when a species becomes extinct it is not likely that the conditions which led to its development will ever again be present on the earth.

Much questioning, discussing, reading, and exploring of the environment will be needed if you are to help your children understand the significance for them of the feeling expressed by the statement, "I am the caretaker of my environment."

Perhaps you have a few children who seem enthusiastic about space fiction. After listening to some of their spontaneous remarks, you wonder if they have enough information to distinguish between fact and fiction. You may decide to help these children explore some of the accumulated information concerning the universe. Many times what is known in an area of science is as interesting and exciting as the product of anyone's imagination.

You may want your boys and girls to learn something about magnetism but have been unable to fit it into any of their other experiences. Do not hesitate to make magnets available to your group. Most children find magnets interesting. You will discover that once your children are familiar with magnets they will find uses for them in their work and play.

Help in evaluating your efforts

Teachers often ask, "How can I tell whether I have planned a good science program for my boys and girls?" One check which seems useful is to ask the question, "Have I planned experiences which will help children to broaden their concepts of space, time, change, adaptation, variety, interrelationships, and energy?"

Another and possibly more valuable check is the continuous evaluation of growth in desirable behavior of your group and of its individual members. You may wish to refer to the list of suggested indications of growth found on pages 5-6. Such an evaluation will give you help in knowing the kinds of experiences the group as a whole needs. It will also help you to guide the work of individual boys and girls.

Sometimes it may be difficult to understand why children in a given problem-solving situation seem so limited in their suggestions. Yet if the children's experiences in the areas from which they should draw suggestions are examined, it may be found that they are quite meager. Those children who have had broad experiences with many different materials often are very resourceful when confronted with problems. But if a child has never seen or heard of a magnet, a dry cell, or a pulley, he cannot be expected to suggest their use in solving a problem. If he has never seen or used a siphon, he is not likely to suggest the use of one to clean the waste from the surface of the sand in an aquarium. Neither will he know how to plant and care for a cactus or geranium if he has had no experiences with plants. How children attack problems may give you one of your best clues as to what experiences to plan for the group.

Children need a wide variety of experiences. If they are to be resourceful, they must have an opportunity to explore many different kinds of materials and phenomena. Some of this exploration may follow suggestions made by the children themselves. You will wish to encourage individual thought and initiative whenever it is practical to do so. The following three criteria may be of help as you consider a child's proposal.

1. *Safety.* Is it safe for all children present and for property?
2. *Conservation behavior.* Does it violate good conservation behavior?
3. *Availability of necessary materials.* Are all of the needed materials available?

If a proposal does not violate any of the above criteria, you may wish to allow it to be tested. Children's proposals have many values. Proposals should not be discarded simply because they do not seem to you to show the desired point clearly. Often when a child's proposal is carried out, it does help to clarify a point for him. When such is not the case a short period of evaluation might be of value. Such questions as "How might the experience have been changed to make it more meaningful?" may bring other good proposals. If conducted without embarrassing the child whose proposal is being discussed, an evaluation discussion might be most valuable in sharpening his ability to check through a proposal more carefully.

Are you concerned because your children are not all interested in the same experiences? Try not to be. Suppose all of the children participated in the same experience. They would not all take the same things from it. What each individual takes from a given experience is determined by many factors. Three of these factors are previous experiences, present needs, and current interests. This means that not all children need the same experiences at the same time. On the other hand, do not hesitate to provide some experiences for an entire class. It is likely that each will profit in his own way from experiences that are well planned and carried out. But try not to expect all to get the same thing from any given experience.

Do you teach fifth or sixth grade and find that your boys and girls tell you they have studied all the areas of science you had planned to explore with them? Don't be too quick to change your plans. Try out some "old" experiences and listen to their discussions of the phenomena involved. They may find it is fun to explore new relationships related to previous experiences. Five-year-olds and eleven-year-olds may both watch the experiment of putting an egg in a bottle. The five-year-old may react first with, "Do it again," perhaps followed by, "Let me do it." Here learning is on an experiential level, concerned chiefly with manipulation, seeing, and feeling. This may be a very worth-while experience for young children. The older children may also be interested in repeating the experience. But most of them will be doing much more thinking and searching for relationships between this and previous experiences. Some will be watching and figuring out hypotheses to explain the action of the egg. If these boys and girls have had other experiences with heating air and with air pressure they may formulate correct hypotheses. If they have not had enough experiences to help them propose explanations, you may wish to suggest other experiences rather than giving them an explanation.

As you work with more mature children you may occasionally need to remind yourself that manipulative experiences are not ends in themselves. They should be planned with larger objectives in mind. For example, putting an egg in a bottle can be more than an exercise in manipulation. It is an opportunity to observe that when air is heated it expands and some of the warm air escapes from the bottle. What happens to air when it is heated and cooled is fundamental to the understanding of winds. The egg experience and other manipulative experiences dealing with the heating and cooling of air are only a part of the many experiences which will help children to build an understanding of winds.

Teachers often ask, "How do I know when and in what detail to answer a child's question?" There is no absolute answer to this question. Knowing the background of your children and the resources available to them are two things that will help you to know when to answer a child's question. If in working out his own answer the child will gain valuable experiences in the use of authoritative materials or the manipulation of materials, or will have an opportunity to grow in some other way, then it may be wise to withhold an answer and help him to find out for himself. But if the answer is one which the child needs in order to proceed with the work at hand, so that a delay at this point would not be helpful, then it may be desirable either to give him the needed information or help him to find it quickly.

The amount of detail to give in an answer is also hard to determine. Some teachers have found it helpful to give a little information and then pause. If the children follow this and can offer some ideas toward further exploration of the question, then there may be continued discussion. If the children are satisfied, they may do nothing to gain further information at that time. They may return to the topic at a later time, however, and be ready to carry the discussion much further.

As you finish reading this section on planning, do you find yourself thinking somewhat as follows? "I should like to help my boys and girls to have more experiences in the area of science. But how can I when I have no equipment?" If these are your thoughts, perhaps the point of view expressed and the suggestions offered in the next chapter will help to remove this last barrier preventing you and your children from enjoying many shared science experiences.

CHAPTER THREE

Equipment—Its Selection and Care

Through reading and talking one may learn what others think and what they have discovered through experimentation and research. This is a valuable type of learning for it has enabled succeeding generations of men to build on what earlier men have learned. Children need opportunities to read and to talk with those who have interesting information to share. But children also need many experiences in which they can explore actual phenomena in their own environment. Some of this exploration will require the manipulation and use of equipment. ("Equipment" in this chapter means all materials needed for an experience.) By using equipment children can do more than read or study about science; they can actually explore some science phenomena. Both reading and doing are important parts of well-planned science experiences.

Science equipment in the elementary school should be safe; it should be simple; and whenever possible and practical it should come from the environment of children and they should have a part in securing and caring for it.

Equipment should be safe

Safety is perhaps the most important single criterion you can use for the selection of equipment to be used by children. For example, in some books for children and also for teachers of children, hydrochloric acid and sulphuric acid are listed for use in certain experiences. In some of these experiences vinegar may be successfully used. In other experiences vinegar is not a useful substitute for one of the stronger acids.

However, since concepts develop as the result of many experiences, usually occurring over a long period of time, children will not be handicapped by a postponement of those experiences using acids that are stronger than vinegar. There is time enough for such experiences when children have more mature judgment and have developed skill in the manipulation of equipment. Vinegar is the only acid suitable for use in the elementary school classroom. It is safe, for it is not strong enough to burn the skin or destroy clothing. Vinegar has the added advantage of being rather easily available in the environment of children.

The use of regular 110-volt electric current as found in most buildings and homes is not safe for children to use in their experimentation. "But," you may say, "electric current is within the home and school environment of most children. They should be taught how to use it in school." It is true that one uses electric current when he plugs in a lamp, toaster, radio, or any one of many other devices, and that such an activity may normally be considered to be safe. There are unusual circumstances, however, when even the use of electric current in these ways is not safe. Furthermore, there is a difference between "experimenting with" and "using" as applied to 110-volt electric current. Almost all children of school age know about turning light switches on and off, and most know how to plug in radios, lamps, and the like. But many children would like to do more than this. Some children of elementary school age would like to work with putting lights and a door bell in their playhouse or store. Others would like footlights on their puppet stage. Still others would like to make telegraph sets and motors using the principle of the electromagnet. All of these experiences require a source of electricity. While 110-volt electric current is not recommended, 1½-volt and 6-volt dry cells may be used with safety to supply the needed electricity.

Because of the cost of the 1½-volt dry cells and their relatively short period of usefulness in the classroom, some teachers have felt the need for another source of electricity. This problem has been met in different ways. Some have used the 110-volt current by installing a transformer in the circuit. This may work satisfactorily at school, but what about the child who wants to make a motor or light circuit at home and has no transformer? If he truly understands the function of the transformer, he will not attempt to use the 110-volt current at home. He will wait for either a transformer or dry cells before trying out his

Equipment—Selection and Care

motor or other device. But suppose he wants to try his motor and remembers only that at school current from the wall outlet was used? Is he not likely to plug his motor into one of the wall outlets in his own home? Many children in our country spend two or more hours at home in the afternoon after school, and many more hours than that on the week-ends, without any adult in the home. If this is true in your community, would you not be taking an unnecessary and undesirable risk in using 110-volt current in your classroom to experiment with electromagnets and light circuits?

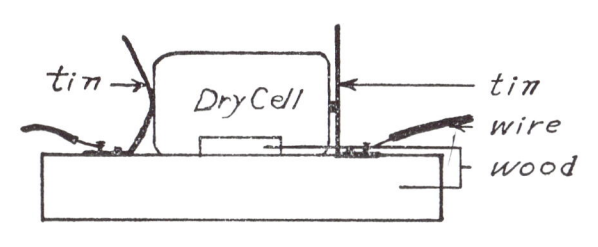

Holder for Flashlight Battery

Another alternative is to use less expensive dry cells. The small cells used in standard-size flashlights are much less expensive than the large 1½-volt cells. They have been used successfully as a source of electric current for light and bell circuits and for electromagnets. By soldering a short piece of copper wire to the center of the top and another short piece of copper wire to the center of the bottom of a flashlight cell, children will be able to connect and disconnect wires easily and safely. If soldering is not available, connections can be made using tin cut from a tin can.

There are two ways in which a child might be hurt when using dry cells. If there is a short circuit, the wire will become very hot. By holding on to the wire long enough one would be burned. Children with normal reflexes, however, will not hold such hot wires long enough to be severely burned. If a child should drop a 1½-volt cell on his foot, it would hurt but probably not cause serious injury.

The use of fire should be considered whenever one is examining science experiences for the safety factor. Policies in schools vary from those in which a match or any other source of flame is prohibited to those in which each teacher makes his or her own decisions about the use of fire. It is suggested that safety matches be used both at school and at home and that time be taken to help children learn to use matches correctly. By working with parents a unified approach can be made to helping children learn to use matches. It is possible to establish conditions under which it is safe to use matches. If these conditions are always established at home and at school, there is little likelihood that children will find it necessary to use matches improperly or in the "wrong" places. This problem differs from that discussed in the use of electric current. In working with matches the effort is made to teach the correct way of using a common object found in most homes. In working with electricity it is also important to teach the correct use of house current to operate appliances. But it is unwise to suggest the use of house current for experimentation by children in elementary schools.

The use of glass in the elementary school should be considered when thinking about safety. Opinions vary greatly on this point. Some believe that if children are to have experiences in science they must use the equipment of the scientists. The people who hold this view buy test tubes, beakers, glass funnels, glass graduates and cylinders, flasks, thistle tubes, and glass tubing for use in the elementary school classroom. Let us look at this a moment. Much of this kind of glass equipment is fragile, and difficult to replace when broken. Do you as a classroom teacher feel at ease in using this kind of equipment? Perhaps not. There are many elementary classroom teachers who feel much more at ease using Pyrex dishes of various sizes, Pyrex nursing bottles, metal and plastic funnels, metal measuring cups, milk bottles, gallon jars, either paper or plastic soda straws, and plastic tubing. And many who can themselves use the more technical glassware with ease realize that it is easier for children to handle durable dishes and other materials like those they have learned to use at home. Where practical, many teachers buy plastic or metal rather than glass equipment.

It would be difficult for children to carry out some worth-while experiences without using glass. But preference should be given to that glass equipment which is easily handled by children and which is the least fragile. Covering the sharp edges of glass with some form of tape which will adhere to the glass will add strength and help to prevent cut fingers.

It is unrealistic to think that one can develop a rich program in the elementary school without some risk. But it is essential to consider safety when making choices in buying equipment.

Equipment should be simple

It is important that science equipment be as simple as is practical. This not only enables young children to use the materials but also makes it easier for them to see and to understand the relationships between pieces of equipment. For example, a knife-blade switch is one of the simplest that can be used by children working with dry cells to complete a bell circuit. In this kind of switch a child can see when the circuit is closed and when it is open. In contrast, this can be seen in a doorbell switch only when the switch is taken apart.

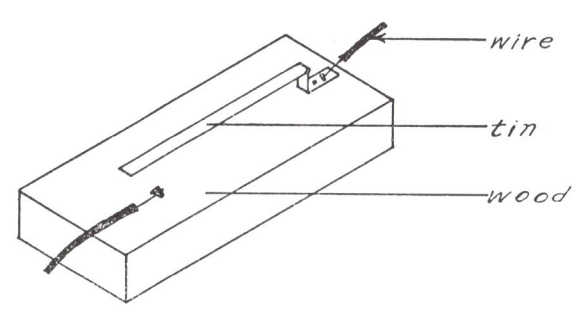

Knife Blade Switch

Another rather important advantage of using simple equipment in the classroom is that children who wish to work at home can often secure materials like those used at school. If children see only the technical pieces of equipment used at school, many will be unable to figure out useable substitutes from the materials available to them in their environment.

Whenever possible, equipment to be used in science experiences in the elementary school should come from the environment of children. It is important that children have an opportunity to handle and to manipulate equipment rather than always being spectators. If the equipment is familiar to children many will be able to handle it with ease. If equipment comes from the local environment it will not only be more accessible than equipment that must be ordered from a distance but it will also be more easily replaced if used up or broken.

There is much to be gained by helping children feel they are active participants in the preparation for science experiences. The challenge of making and improvising equipment is good preparation for resourcefulness, and helps to take the doing of experiments out of the "cook book" category. If a child or teacher understands the purpose of the experience and the principle to be shown, he can often make use of available equipment or construct what he needs.

Some teachers use part of their funds to buy basic tools and raw materials with which children can work to construct part of the equipment they need. They have found that some of their children show greater interest in science when they have a part in planning and working out ideas. For example, when a child needs a knife-blade switch, he can easily make one from a block of wood, three nails, and a strip of tin cut from a tin can. Similarly when he needs a stand from which objects may be suspended he can build one. Directions for building three general-purpose stands may be found on pages 41-43. Other types of stands may be constructed using sections of broom and mop handles.

Using equipment made by a child helps to build in him a sense of individual worth. However, little is to be gained by the use of poor equipment. If a student-built stand or other equipment does not serve the purpose as well as commercial products, and if the latter are available, they should be used. But equipment does not have to be expensive in order to be good. Tools and adequate raw materials with which to work, rather than expensive, elaborate, and often complicated equipment, are preferred by many teachers who provide rich experiences for their children.

Some special science equipment is needed

While there is much equipment which can be brought from home by children, bought in the local stores, and made in the classroom or at home, there is some special science equipment which you will find useful. For example, a tuning fork will be invaluable in the study of sound. You will be able to do some things with a tuning fork which you will be unable to do with substitute materials. Magnets will also be desirable equipment in most elementary schools. You will probably help any group studying magnets to magnetize materials which will retain their magnetism for several hours or longer. However, your program will be limited if all the magnets you have are the ones you can

General Purpose Stand No. 1

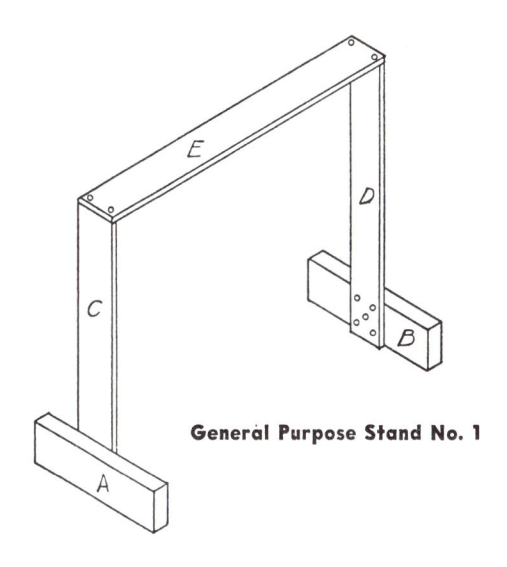

You may find this stand desirable because of its simple construction and adaptability. It may be used with both "feet" resting on the same table, or with each "foot" resting on a different table. In the latter position it can be used for hanging objects longer than 14", such as a pendulum.

Almost any kind of available wood may be used. The measurements given here are only suggestions. You may wish to change them to better fit your needs.

Materials needed:
   A and B: 7" long, 2" wide, ¼" thick
   C and D: 14" long, 2" wide, ¼" thick
   E: 16" long, 2" wide, ¼" thick
   14 1" nails
   1 small hook

Directions:
   Nail C to A using 5 nails spaced as in the drawing of D and B.
   Nail D to B using 5 nails spaced as in the drawing.
   Nail E to C and E to D using 2 nails in each end.
   Put the small hook in the middle of the under surface of E.
   Use sandpaper to smooth off all the edges and surfaces.
   Paint desired color.

Note: This stand can be made stronger by using screws in the place of nails and by using wood or metal braces where E and C and where E and D join.

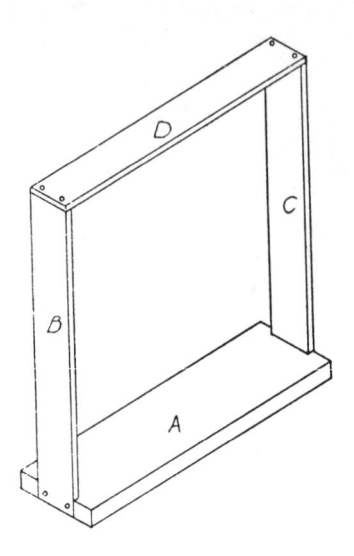

General Purpose Stand No. 2

This stand is somewhat more difficult to make than No. 1 because of the cut out places in each end of A. It has the advantage of being stronger, especially if screws are used.

Almost any kind of available wood may be used. The measurements given here are only suggestions. You may wish to change them to better fit your needs.

Materials needed:

    A: 14" long, 4" wide, ¾" thick
    B and C: 15" long, 2" wide, ¼" thick
    D: 13½" long, 2" wide, ¼" thick
    8 1" nails or screws
    1 small hook

Directions:

    Cut out the places in A.
    Nail or screw B to A and C to A.
    Nail or screw D to B and D to C.
    Put the small hook in the middle of the under surface of D.
    Use sandpaper to smooth off all the edges and surfaces.
    Paint desired color.

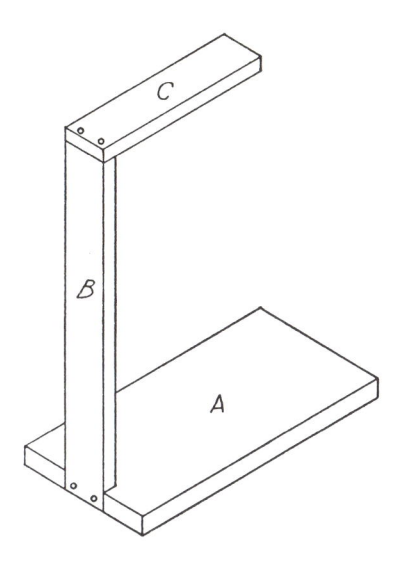

General Purpose Stand No. 3

This stand is easy to make except for the cut out place in **A**. It is stronger if made with screws. Almost any kind of available wood may be used. The measurements given here are only suggestions. You may wish to change them to better fit your needs.

Materials needed:

    A: 12" long, 6" wide, ¾" thick.
    B: 15" long, 2" wide, ½" thick
    C: 8" long, 2" wide, ½" thick
    4 1" nails or screws
    1 small hook

Directions:

    Cut out the place in **A**.
    Nail or screw B to A.
    Nail or screw C to B.
    Put the small hook 1" from the free end and 1" from the side of C.
    Use sandpaper to smooth off all the edges and surfaces.
    Paint desired color.

make by stroking a commercial magnet you have borrowed. Magnets can often be bought in local stores. And sometimes they may be purchased from those in the community who salvage parts from used cars, household appliances, or other equipment.

Simple pulleys can be made from spools of various kinds. But you will find it helpful to buy several small double pulleys and a number of single pulleys of the kind used on clotheslines if you wish to provide a variety of experiences with pulleys for your boys and girls. Often the kinds of pulleys found in local stores will be easier for children to work with than many of the demonstration pulleys sold by scientific supply houses. The groove in the wheel of the demonstration pulley is often so small that it is difficult for children to get the cord to stay in place.

If you wish to help children learn how a thermostat works, a compound bar will be useful. A compound bar is made of two unlike pieces of metal fused or held together with brads so that each side of the bar is a different metal. Sometimes these can be bought from a salvage dealer. Some salvage dealers will be interested and able to explain to a group of children how the piece of metal was used in the automatic device in an electric refrigerator, electric stove, or other appliance from which it was taken. Such an experience would be more meaningful for most children than using a demonstration compound bar in the classroom.

In the study of electricity, equipment such as doorbells, dry cells, light sockets, bulbs, and wire will usually need to be bought. In some groups, however, you may find that certain children have such equipment at home which they would be willing to bring to school and share with their classmates.

Before buying or collecting science equipment, you may wish to plan the science areas and some of the experiences you wish your children to have in each of these areas. Then you will have a better idea of the kind of equipment you need and the importance it will have in your program. In other words, you will have a purpose for the materials you buy. This is quite different from looking at a list of equipment and buying whatever looks interesting. It is also different from buying equipment which has been selected and packaged by someone unfamiliar with your plans and your teaching situation. When you or your school are making plans to buy equipment, it might be helpful to compare the quality, quantity, suitability, and total cost of commercial kits

Equipment—Selection and Care

of equipment with the materials you yourself would select and use. You will probably find that for an equivalent amount of money you can get materials better suited to your program and in greater quantity if you do your own planning and purchasing.

A way of sharing and caring for equipment is needed

You will want to have some equipment in your own classroom all of the time. If you stay in the same school for several years you will be able to build up a supply of useful materials. But there will be other equipment that should be shared by all the school rather than duplicated in several classrooms. This creates the problem of finding a central storage place which is easily accessible to all who wish to use the equipment. To make the system function smoothly one faculty member is usually assigned the responsibility of scheduling and checking equipment.

In some schools a closet or other small room is the science supply room. Other school buildings are so crowded that no such space is available. In some of these buildings cabinets and open shelves are built along the walls of a corridor. Here equipment for science is stored. Sometimes the only available space is in a classroom. In some schools this has not worked too well; it is found that teachers hesitate to go to the room for equipment because of the possibility of disturbing the class. Occasionally it has been found that a teacher in whose room equipment was stored developed a feeling of ownership.

After a storage place for the equipment is decided upon, the next step is to decide the classification under which materials will be most readily available. Some have organized their materials by units for each grade. This sometimes causes complications. For example, a second and a fifth grade may each have a unit in which magnets are needed. Cross referencing and the buying of duplicate materials are ways of handling such problems. Another method of classification is according to areas such as heat, light, sound, magnetism, static electricity, current electricity, machines, air and water, rocks and soils, and plants.

Once the areas of classification have been decided upon, a color may be chosen to represent each of the areas. For example, red may be for heat, yellow for light, blue for electricity, green for plants, and so on. Choose whatever colors are pleasing to you. A paint color chart is sometimes helpful since you will need paint of each color chosen. The paint needs to be of a kind that will adhere to cardboard or wood. Usually one of the less expensive brands of paint will be satisfactory.

You are now ready to collect boxes of all sizes and shapes. Children will be able to help with this part of the project. Some stores in the community may be willing to save boxes for you if you arrange to have them collected regularly. Once you have a supply of boxes, the next job is to select those best suited by size and strength to hold the different pieces of equipment. A committee of upper grade children working with a teacher can often do an excellent job of this.

As soon as an appropriate box for a piece of equipment is located, the color of the box can be quickly determined. For example, doorbells are to be used in the study of electricity. So as soon as a box which will hold the supply of bells is located, it can be handed over to the member of the paint committee who is using the color which will designate electricity. It may be best to remove the materials from each box while the box is being painted. If this is done, care should be taken to arrange the contents of each box so that they can be returned to the proper place as soon as the paint is dry. For some boxes one coat of paint is adequate. Others will need two coats of paint if they are to look neat. After the paint dries and the equipment has been returned to the correct boxes, a label should be made for each box, listing the name and number of each item in it. Labels should be fastened to one side or one end of a box, depending on the position of the box on the shelf. Teachers will find labels useful in checking the equipment before returning it to the supply shelves. The labels will also be helpful to the teacher charged with periodically checking the condition of the equipment.

The color system makes it possible to keep materials together which are frequently used together. It also enables one to collect materials more quickly than if the content of each box or shelf has to be examined to find the needed materials. A system of this kind makes it easy for a teacher or a child to go to the supply cabinet and quickly collect all of the boxes of a given color. Thus, within a few minutes it is possible to have in any classroom all of the materials available for a given area.

Perhaps you are saying something like this to yourself: "That is a lot of bother. I wonder if it is worth it?" This is something you and your co-workers will need to decide for yourselves. Some teachers have found that this kind of housekeeping saves time once the system is established. It has also been found useful in helping to take better care of many items of equipment.

The material in this booklet up to this point has been planned not only to extend your understanding of science but also to increase your readiness for working with boys and girls in the area of science. The next two chapters suggest specific experiences, some of which you will find useful in planning experiences that will help your children to reorganize old concepts and to develop new ones related to the solid, liquid, and gaseous parts of the earth. This selection does not imply that these content areas are more valuable than others. In a small book, it seems advisable to provide a substantial quantity and a wide range of experiences in a few related areas than to treat many areas more superficially.

CHAPTER FOUR

The Solid Part of the Earth

MANY children may have had their first contact with the ground when as tiny infants they were put down on a blanket spread on the ground. Other children must wait until they begin to crawl, and still others must wait until they have learned to walk, before being permitted on the ground. By the time children are in nursery school and kindergarten they have had many experiences with the solid part of the earth. They will probably have learned from falling on the ground that some ground is very hard. They may have had the fun of playing in a sand pile or a sand box. Many have had the fun of letting nice soft mud squash up between their toes, or made wonderful mud pies. The chances are that if they live where there are big rocks, they have had fun climbing them. They may have had the fun of helping an adult work in a garden or flower bed. All these experiences and many more provide a very rich background on which to build concepts.

In their relations with adults some children may have been given a feeling for the value of soil. They may have noticed erosion gullies, or streams muddy with soil after a rain. Other children may not have had experiences which would help them to understand the value of soil. Learning about the care of soil will be new to them.

At an early age some children begin to show an interest in rocks and minerals and to collect "pretty rocks." This may be only a temporary interest based on a common activity that can be shared with congenial adults or peers. The collecting of rocks, however, may become an activity based on the individual's own interest and initiative. Whatever the origin of the interest, it is possessed by most youngsters at some time in their childhood. Evidence of children's contact with rocks because of their own or an adult's interest can be observed in almost any elementary school classroom at some time or other during the school year. In rooms or corridors of some schools large exhibits are on display. In many classrooms rocks may be found on a table, on a book shelf, in individual student lockers, or in the pocket of a young enthusiast.

As a child matures, the idea of "pretty rocks" may give way to an interest in different kinds of rocks. Sometimes children learn from their teacher or some other interested adult the ways of making simple tests for identification of rocks. They may also learn one of the acceptable ways of labeling rocks. The adult collectors of rocks and minerals are frequently those who begin this hobby at an early age. The interest of a young person in rocks and minerals may lead him to choose a vocation that will allow for continued study.

It is desirable that children be helped to see the need for wise use of the rocks and minerals of the earth. Many of these are very old. They were formed from minerals and rocks that were on the earth earlier and that were weathered and eroded. It is believed that the original rocks and minerals of the earth were formed when liquid lava became solid. They were igneous rocks (from the Latin word *ignis*, meaning "fire"). As particles from these igneous rocks were eroded by wind and water, they were redeposited. Some of these particles were deposited as sediment over the land and others were deposited along river banks, in deltas, in lakes, and in oceans. During millions of years this sediment was covered by other sediment and was gradually changed into sandstone or shale. This is a process that goes on continuously, but it is very, very slow. If men are wasteful, they may destroy the rocks and minerals much faster than they can be formed and thus lead to a real scarcity of some rock and mineral materials. Men are dependent directly or indirectly on rocks and minerals for the metals they use; for many of their chemicals; for building stones and many other building materials; for the gems they value; and even for the food they eat. Men must therefore learn to use these resources wisely if they are to survive. Children should learn at an early age that conservation means wise use of resources rather than no use of such materials.

In addition to our dependence on rocks and minerals for many of our physical needs, we are in part dependent on them for a satisfaction of our aesthetic needs. It is good to call to the attention of children the beauty of the natural rock, mineral, and soil formations in their own regions. Our land is not all alike, but every natural region has its beauty. Unfortunately people in their work and play have not always added to the beauty of a region. Children may be helped to become sensitive to the beauty of natural earth formations. With guidance and help, a group of children may acquire a feeling of responsibility for their environment.

Because of the differences in the background experiences of children, you, the teacher, might profit by allowing the children to talk informally about their experiences, observations, and concepts in this area of study. Having done this, you will be better able to select from the following material those activities which will be most helpful to the boys and girls. You will find that the experiences suggested here are grouped under two headings: Rocks and Minerals, and Soils and Erosion.* It is not necessary that they be studied in the order presented, or that all of the experiences be provided for every member of a group.

ROCKS AND MINERALS

Experience R-1. To look at rocks and minerals in their natural surroundings

If the school is located near any exposed rock, you and the children may plan to visit such areas at different times during your study. Some good places to visit would be street or road cuts, eroded gulleys, quarry walls, or construction excavations. Small groups of children or individual children together with their parents or other adults may make additional visits to natural rock formations.

Some of the things which the children may observe are (1) the color of rocks, (2) the presence or absence of layers, (3) whether the rock appears to be of one kind or whether it has rock of different color and appearance running through it, (4) whether there are many different rocks or whether all of the rock is one big mass, and (5) something of the degree of hardness of the rock.

* Experiences on Rocks and Minerals will be numbered R-1, R-2, etc.; those on Soils and Erosion, S-1, S-2, etc. Experiences on Air and Water, in Chapter Five, will be numbered A-1, A-2, etc., and W-1, W-2, etc.

In class discussions the children should be encouraged to express their observations. Those who like to draw may use sketches or paintings to record what they have seen.

If there has been sufficient observation, the children will be likely to make some of the following generalizations about rocks: (1) there are many different kinds of rocks, (2) rocks do not all look alike, (3) rocks have different colors, (4) some rocks are smooth and others have sharp edges, (5) rocks are not all the same size, (6) rocks are not all of the same hardness. Some children may also begin to ask questions about how rocks are formed.

Experience R-2. To practice conservation in the collecting of rocks and minerals

After children have observed many different rocks and minerals in their natural surroundings, they may wish to make a collection of rocks of the kinds found in the region in which they live.

It would be helpful for the children to discuss their purposes for collecting before they begin. This discussion should be directed so as to help the children develop a regard for their environment. They should be helped to see that rocks have an important place in the environment and that all of any one kind should not be removed from a site. Since the object is to have many different kinds of rocks to study, there is little value in having twenty or thirty rocks of the same kind.

Boys and girls should be helped through this experience to develop a wholesome outlook toward the wise use of the environment. The use of only one or two similar rocks for study in the classroom should help to show that wise use means not taking more than you need, and not taking all of any one kind of thing from the environment.

If the discussion has been made meaningful to the children, they will be willing to collect only one or two samples of a given kind of rock or mineral. To the few children who will collect too many rocks of a kind, some individual help may be given by you. These children should not be embarrassed or hurried, but should be helped and given time to incorporate this new idea into their thinking and their actions.

If rocks from a wide area are brought in, it might be interesting to keep a record of where each sample was collected. It may be pointed out that this is something most collectors do.

Experience R-3. To group rocks and minerals

What a group of children will do in organizing and studying rocks and minerals in a collection will depend on their maturity, previous experience, and interest. Reading in books and in other authoritative written materials about rocks may help to stimulate interest and help to give the direction for future activity.

The following are some ways that children might find useful in grouping the rocks and minerals they have collected.

a. TO USE SIMPLE TESTS FOR DETERMINING THE HARDNESS OF ROCKS AND MINERALS. Rocks and minerals differ in hardness. This difference is due in part to the materials of which they are formed and in part to the conditions under which they were formed. For example, some sandstone that is formed under water is much harder than some sandstone formed on dry land.

It is likely that some children will be content to group their rocks under such names as "soft rocks" and "hard rocks." "Soft rocks" would include all those from which they could rub particles with their hands. All those from which particles cannot be rubbed with their hands would be called "hard rocks."

Other children may be ready to learn a few simple ways of testing for several degrees of hardness of rocks or minerals. The children are likely to find that no two samples are alike in hardness. The following tests should be helpful in making rough groupings:

(1) See which samples you can scratch with your fingernail. Put all of these together. They are your softest rocks and minerals.

(2) See which samples you can scratch with a copper penny. If you have any such samples, put them together. These are your next hardest rocks and minerals.

For the next two tests you will need a piece of steel. A knife blade can be used. If children use a sharp knife, they may need the help of someone who handles a knife well.

(3) This time see how many of the samples you have not grouped can be scratched with a piece of steel. Now see how many of these will not scratch glass. (For this test of course only rocks that have an edge to scratch with can be tested.) Those samples that will not scratch glass, but which you can scratch with a piece of steel, are your third group of

rocks and minerals. They are harder than those that could be scratched with a copper penny.

(4) Your next hardest group of rocks and minerals is composed of those which you can scratch with steel, and with which you can scratch glass.

(5) If a piece of known quartz is available, try all of the samples that you have left to see if any of them will scratch it. All of those that will scratch quartz belong in your hardest rocks and minerals.

Scientists use a scale of one to ten in determining the hardness of minerals. If some of the more mature children are interested in learning this scale, it may be found in most physical geology books.[1] Labeled specimens may be bought from one of the scientific supply houses listed on page 140.

b. To IDENTIFY LIMESTONE AND MARBLE. Put one-fourth to one-half cup of vinegar in a small pan or glass dish that can be heated. Heat the vinegar. It is not necessary for it to boil. Remove the dish or pan from the heat. Now put a corner of the sample down in the vinegar. If small bubbles appear, the sample is either limestone or marble. The bubbles are carbon dioxide gas. If the test is made using vinegar at room temperature, some bubbles will usually appear. Heat speeds up the chemical reaction so that the bubbles are more numerous and easier for children to observe.

Limestone is transformed into marble by heat and pressure. This accounts for the similar action of these two kinds of rocks.

c. To GROUP TOGETHER ROCKS FORMED UNDER SIMILAR CONDITIONS. Some children might be stimulated to further study and try to group together those rocks which were formed under similar conditions. There are three basic ways in which rocks are formed. One is by the deposit of materials as sediments. Rocks formed in this way are called sedimentary rocks. The second way in which rocks are formed is by the cooling of liquid lava. Rocks formed in this way are called igneous rocks. A third way in which rocks are formed is by sedimentary or igneous rocks being under such extreme heat and pressure that they are changed into new kinds of rocks. These new kinds of rocks are called metamorphic rocks.

[1] Chester R. Longwell, Adolph Knopf, and Richard F. Flint, *Physical Geology*, 3rd ed. (New York: John Wiley and Sons, Inc., 1948), p. 551.

Sometimes children make use of labeled collections, books, or museum displays to identify their samples. If this is done, they will be able to group all their sandstone, limestone, and shale together as sedimentary rock. The samples of granite, many other rocks that contain large and small crystals, and the glass-like rocks may all be grouped together as rocks that were formed by heat. They are igneous rocks. The samples of schist, slate, marble, quartzite, gneiss and the like may be grouped together as rocks that were formed from other rocks under extreme heat and pressure. These are metamorphic rocks.

It might help you to remember that in the study of rocks emphasis should be put on the importance of rocks as a part of our environment. It is not important that children learn the names of rocks. You should not be embarrassed when you are not able to name all of the rocks brought in by the children. Many good geologists, those who have made the study of rocks their life work, do not name all rocks immediately upon sight.

This study of the ways rocks are formed may help children build concepts related to change and time. That is, some sedimentary and igneous rocks have been changed into metamorphic rocks. The realization of the time it took for this change to occur would help children to expand their thinking about the age of the rocks in their region and possibly about the age of the earth.

Experience R-4. To see how some sedimentary rocks might have been formed

Sedimentary rocks are those formed by the deposition of materials carried by wind or water. The materials which were deposited to form the first sedimentary rocks came from igneous rocks. The materials which are now being deposited and will form sedimentary rocks are particles eroded from igneous, sedimentary, and metamorphic rocks. The three most numerous kinds of sedimentary rocks are shale, sandstone, and limestone. You should be guided by the experiences and interests of the children, and by the region in which you live, in selecting and adapting the most suitable experiences among those which follow.

These experiences may be used to help children expand their concept of time in relation to the age of rocks. They may also be used in the development of concepts related to change, variety, and interrelationships. Many changes occur in the formation of sedimentary rocks. The sedimentary rocks of the earth vary in kind, depth, and extent of formation, and in color. There is an interrelationship between the physical forces of wind and water and the formation of sedimentary rocks.

a. TO SEE HOW SHALE MIGHT HAVE BEEN FORMED. Shale is the most abundant of the sedimentary rocks. It is formed from clay and silt and may be deposited by either wind or water. Because of the small size of the particles they are usually the last of the solid materials to be deposited by the wind or water. Children can see this if they put some garden soil into a bottle that is about half full of water. Shake the bottle about fifty times. When the soil particles settle, one should be able to see that the coarse parts settle first and the finer particles of clay and silt settle next. Sometimes organic matter, decaying animal or plant material, will remain at the surface of the water for some time. This is similar to the order in which shale is deposited by natural forces.

If there is a sample of shale available, put a few drops of water on it and smell the rock. There should be an odor similar to that of wet soil.

b. TO SEE HOW SANDSTONE MIGHT HAVE BEEN FORMED. Sandstones are the second most numerous of the sedimentary rocks. They are made up primarily of quartz particles. Most sandstone is formed under water. Some, however, is formed on land where it has been deposited by wind. If you live in a desert region, you may be very conscious of wind-deposited sand. If you live near an ocean, a lake, or a river, you may find that some of the children have observed the depositing and the shifting of sand by the water.

Children might find it interesting to see ways in which the deposition is altered by changing certain conditions. If grains of sand of different colors and different size are available, they will be useful, but they are not necessary. Secure a large-mouth glass container. An aquarium tank is fine for this, but a large-mouth glass jar can be used. Have a supply of sand ready. Make a trough out of boards or cut a tin can lengthwise and use half of it as a trough.

Put about two inches of water in the glass container. Hold the trough so that one end extends over the edge of the glass container for about an inch. The other end should be held or supported so that its height can be changed. If several are doing the experiment together, one person can hold the trough with the upper end near a yardstick so that the height can be noted.

Now sprinkle some of the coarse sand along on the trough. With a small stream of water from a bottle, teakettle, or watering can, wash the sand from the trough into the glass jar or dish. Notice how the pieces of sand scatter out and settle to the bottom. If sand of different size grains is being used, notice also that the larger grains sink first. Repeat the procedure, using sands of different colors. Vary the angle of the trough and note the difference in the way the sand is scattered. Vary the size of the stream of water and note the difference in the way the sand is scattered. After the sand grains have settled, look in through the side of the glass container. Layers similar to those seen in some pieces of sandstone should be visible. If the sand is all of the same color, it will more closely resemble pieces of sandstone that are red, gray, or cream-colored.

If the glass container has a very large opening, the end of the trough may be held beneath the surface of the water while the sand is washed in with more water. See what different results you can get by varying the angle of the trough, and by varying the amount of water used to pour onto the sand. The results obtained in this experiment would be similar to what happens when a river carries sand into a lake, sea, or ocean, but on a much smaller scale.

What has been made is not sandstone. For in addition to the settling of sand grains in the water there must be either a cementing substance present, a drying of the sediments, or pressure on the sediments from above in order for the formation of sandstone to take place. Also, not all sandstone is made under water. Sometimes sand is carried by the wind and dropped in a given area. This may be repeated many times. In time, if the weight of the sand becomes great enough, the sand near the bottom will begin to change into sandstone. As the sand continues to be piled up on the surface, more sandstone is formed beneath the surface.

c. TO EXAMINE LIMESTONE AS AN AID IN UNDERSTANDING HOW IT MIGHT HAVE BEEN FORMED. If you live in a region where limestone is visible along the banks of streams, in excavations, or along road cuts, perhaps you and your group can observe limestone in its natural location.

Rocks and Minerals

Limestone is the third most abundant of the sedimentary rocks. It is formed only under water. It may be formed by the chemical settling out of calcium carbonate which was dissolved from deposits through which rivers flow on their way to lakes and oceans. Limestone formed in this way contains very fine grains and appears very uniform in composition. Perhaps you can secure samples of this kind of limestone for your group to examine. Limestone may also be formed from the accumulation of the shells and bones of dead sea animals. Coquina is a limestone that is made of an abundance of shells loosely cemented. Samples of coquina and of limestone which contain fossils of shells, bones, and impressions of animals that lived long ago would help your children to become familiar with this type of limestone. Some limestone formations are composed of a mixture of the fine grain calcium carbonate, microscopic shells, and larger shells.

Experience R-5. To see how mineral crystals might have been formed

Rocks are made of minerals. In some rocks the mineral crystals are larger and more visible than in others. In looking at rocks in their natural surroundings and also when collecting rocks, children probably will see some crystals. Mineral crystals may be transparent (objects can be identified through them), translucent (light can be seen through them but objects cannot be identified), or opaque (light is not visible through them). The forms in which any one mineral may be found will vary, depending on the conditions under which it originated.

The size of the crystalline mass in any rock is dependent upon the length of time that the minerals stay in solution. In rocks where the time that minerals are in solution is very short, there are tiny crystals. In the glassy igneous rocks, cooling and thus solidification took place so rapidly that crystals did not form. In some of the granites, cooling and the resulting solidification took place so slowly that large crystals were formed. As long as solutions are present in the rocks, smaller crystals are combined to form larger crystals. Thus the size of crystals found in rock is an indication of the rate at which it dried and became solid.

a. To make soda crystals. Take a small dish that can be heated and put in one-half cup of water. Slowly add baking soda to the water and stir. Continue to add soda and stir until no more soda will dissolve. Put the dish over an electric hot plate, alcohol lamp, or other source of heat. When the solution gets hot and all of the soda is dissolved, add more soda a little at a time. Continue to stir the solution. When no more soda will dissolve, set the clear solution aside and allow it to cool slowly.

Soda crystals should begin to form around the dish at the level of the liquid as the solution cools. If strings are suspended in the liquid soon after the dish is taken from the heat, crystals will form around the string. If it is difficult to get the string to stay down in the liquid, paper clips may be fastened to the end of the string. Small pebbles may also be used for this purpose.

This container of crystals should be kept if part *b* of this experience is to be done.

Crystals of table salt, sugar, and copper sulphate may be made in the same way that the soda crystals were.

b. To MAKE CRYSTALS OF DIFFERENT SIZES. If *a* above has not been done, then it should be done now. If *a* above was done and the crystals kept, repeat the experiment down to the point where you are told, "When no more soda will dissolve, set the clear solution aside." This time, instead of letting the solution cool slowly, put the dish into a dish or pan of cold water when it is taken from the stove. If ice is available, it may be used to cool the water even more rapidly. Crystals will again form around the dish at the level of the liquid.

Look closely at the crystals formed in each dish. Are there differences in the size of the crystals? Set both dishes aside where they will not be disturbed. Look at them the next day. If sugar is used, it may take several days or weeks before crystals begin to form. They are very beautiful and worth waiting for. In the dish that was allowed to cool slowly there should be small crystals near the top and much larger crystals in the bottom of the dish. The crystals in the dish that cooled rapidly should all be small.

c. To EXAMINE ROCKS AND MINERALS FOR CRYSTALS. Look at samples of rocks and minerals that contain crystals. A hand lens may be found useful in looking at the samples. Are the crystals large or small? If the crystals are large, the rock probably cooled or dried very slowly. If the crystals are small, the rock probably cooled or dried very rapidly.

Experience R-6. To record observations or interpretations of rock formations

Some children derive benefit from recording observations or interpretations in ways other than writing. It is well to provide children with opportunities for a variety of experiences in record-making. It is believed that the three methods of making records suggested below will vary in value and interest for different children. They are included because some may find that they can express their information better in one of these ways than they can by using words.

a. By making drawings. If it is practical in your teaching situation, some children may be given the opportunity to make sketches of rock formations while they are actually observing the formations. In other situations the children may need to work using only what they can remember as a guide.

Young children may be content with recording the large over-all view of the rock. More mature children may be interested in filling in much more detail in their drawings. Occasionally a child may look at drawings in geology books and learn to use similar techniques in his work. The use of color in such work may help to make the drawings more meaningful.

Frequently children's correct conceptions and also their misconceptions, if any, of what is observed can be gained from an examination of their drawings.

b. By making sand pictures. Sand pictures can be made in a shallow pan, box lid, or sand table, depending on how large a picture is desired. They may also be made on pieces of glass with clay used to make a border to hold the sand in place. If desired, this type or the box lid type may be covered with glass. Adhesive tape or some other kind of gummed tape may be used to hold the cover glass in place.

If glass is used, show the children how to handle it by first covering the edges with cloth or paper. It might be best to use pieces of glass about six inches square or smaller, because of the ease in handling small pieces.

There are several ways of actually making the pictures. The first step in one that is usually successful is to cover the area that is to be used with an even layer of sand. The thickness of this layer will be determined by the amount of sand available and the container used. Only a very thin layer, one-eighth to one-fourth inch thick, is needed for most pictures. With a pencil, outline the areas on which you wish to use the different colored sands to show the folding, arching, breaking, and other variations of the layers of rocks that have been observed.

If colored sand is not available, substitutes may be used, such as spices, cocoa, or other materials from the kitchen. Those who save their small pieces of colored chalk will find that these can be easily powdered. One method of doing this is to put the chalk between several folds of paper on the work table and then tap it lightly with a hammer or other solid object. The powdered chalk can then be carefully sprinkled over the background sand to indicate the formation desired. Perhaps other substitutes that are more readily available in the environment may be found. One of the commercial clothing dyes might be used to dye sand the desired color.

c. BY USING CLAY MODELS. If there is a supply of clay, some children will be able to make models of the rock formations they have observed. Clay that is mixed with water or with oil will be suitable. Clays of different colors will add interest to the work. A knife or fine wire may be used to trim the finished model. Care should be exercised in the use of either the knife or the wire.

Experience R-7. To discover what a fossil is

Some children may be familiar with the word *fossil* and have had the experience of hunting fossils. But for many children *fossil* is likely to be a new word that opens up another area to be explored.

A trip to a museum to look at fossils might be a way you could stimulate an interest in fossils. Or if you are teaching in an area where fossils of any kind are easily found, you may wish to plan a trip that would give children an opportunity to observe fossils in their environment. You may plan for collecting one or two fossils of each kind found so that they may be re-examined during your study.

A fossil is any evidence of the existence on earth of a plant or animal that lived a long time ago. There is no exact time at which animal or plant remains become a fossil. Many scientists working in this area have agreed to call any plant or animal remains as much as a hundred thousand years old fossils. Many regard some more recent remains as fossils.

Fossils may be of four kinds: (1) Hardened prints or impressions of plants or animals. This would include such things as footprints, tail marks, trails, burrows of animals, impressions of all or part of an animal's body, and seed, leaf, or bark impressions of plants. (2) Part or all of the preserved body of a plant or an animal. Some of the best examples are entire animals that have been found frozen in ice. Also some insect bodies have been preserved in amber. Skeletons, shells, or other hard parts of an animal body are perhaps the most abundant fossils. (3) Cast of a plant or an animal. Perhaps the casts of ancient clams or other shelled animals are the most common fossils of this type. (4) Petrified remains of a plant or an animal. If children live near or visit an area of petrified forest, this may be the type of fossil with which they are most familiar.

If samples of different fossils are brought in for study, some members of the class may wish to group their collection according to these four kinds of fossils.

This experience is one which can be used to help children broaden their concepts of variety, for there are many different types of each of the four main kinds of fossils. Individual fossils vary greatly in size—from pollen grains and the tiny, sometimes microscopic, shells of foraminifers to tree trunks and large bones of dinosaurs. If you are able to visit a museum, you will have an opportunity to help children actually see some of the great variation in size and structure of fossils.

Experience R-8. To find out where to look for fossils

Fossils may be found in a variety of materials. Sedimentary rock will be found to yield a greater number of fossils than any other kind of rock. Occasionally fossils may be found in metamorphic rock. They are very rarely found in igneous rock. Some fossils have been found frozen in ice, and some have been found in amber or other plant resins. Coal sometimes contains an abundance of plant fossils. In fact, pure coal *is* a fossil!

It may be recalled that igneous rocks are formed from liquid rock that cooled either below or on the surface of the earth. Normally we would not expect to find plant or animal remains in this kind of rock. A very few fossils have been found in areas where cities or villages destroyed by volcanoes have been excavated. Also a few fossils have been found in tuff beds which are of volcanic origin. These are unusual and are thought to have resulted when volcanic dust fell in water containing animals and plants.

Metamorphic rock, if you recall, is made from sedimentary and igneous rock that has been changed by water solutions, gases, heat, and pressure. In most of this kind of rock the fossils, if once present, have usually been destroyed. There have been, however, a few fossils found in metamorphic rock.

The sedimentary rocks have been made by the deposition of sediments. Footprints or tail prints of animals made in soft mud may have been filled by sand or loose soil and thus preserved. If this mud and sand or soil later hardened into rock, the print would be preserved for millions of years. Bones and shells of animals may also be quickly covered and thus the usual decay prevented. If these deposits later harden into rock, they will contain fossils.

Limestone deposits, if of organic origin, frequently contain many fossils. In some areas the fossils are so numerous that fossiliferous limestone is quarried and sold as a highly prized building stone. Some buildings and the bases of some monuments are made in part or wholly from this kind of limestone. It might be interesting for the children to examine buildings in their town to see if any contain fossiliferous limestone.

If children live in a soft-coal mining area, they may be able to find fossils of plants in coal. Or if the school uses large pieces of coal for heating, some of the pieces may be examined for fossils. Pressure frequently destroys fossils. In forming, hard coal is under greater pressure than soft coal. It is unlikely that as many fossils will be found in hard coal as will be found in soft coal.

Although fossils have been found in ice and amber, these are very rare. Children are not likely to be able to have first-hand experiences with fossils of this type. Some children who live where there are deposits of sedimentary rock can have interesting experiences, however, in hunting for fossils. Exposed surfaces of sedimentary rock, road cuts, creek and river beds and banks, quarry walls, and excavations for buildings are good places to hunt for fossils. In the interests of safety, children should not be allowed to visit such places unless an adult is present.

Rocks and Minerals

Experience R-9. To make impressions of leaves and shells

Children will of course not be able to make fossils. But they can get a better idea of how fossil prints might have been made by following one of the suggestions below.

a. BY USING MUD OR CLAY. Make some "mud pies" by mixing soil and water. Drop spoonfuls of this mixture on a piece of cardboard or a wood board. Press a leaf, underside down, on the surface of one of these mud mounds. Let it dry. Remove the leaf and examine the print left in the mud. This is similar to what might happen in soil after a rain or along a river bank.

Press into one of the mud mounds a shell that has been oiled or coated with a thin covering of petroleum jelly. When it has dried, remove the shell. The oil or petroleum jelly should make the removal of the shell easy.

Different objects can be pressed into the mud, and after the mud dries their print will remain. Clay that is mixed with water or oil may be used instead of mud.

b. BY USING PLASTER OF PARIS. Plaster of Paris is not quite as easy to work with as mud or clay, but good prints can be made in it. First put a thin coat of oil or petroleum jelly on the object of which a print is to be made. Now mix about one cup of plaster of Paris with enough water to make a very thick, smooth mixture. Then drop spoonfuls of the mixture out on cardboard or wood board. Before it hardens, press leaves, shells, bones or any other object that has been prepared into the plaster. Let the plaster harden. Remove the object. A good print should be visible.

Experience R-10. To determine the age of rocks by studying their position

Children frequently want to know something about how the age of rocks is determined. The complete answer is very complicated. It is one which is still being studied. As new instruments and new tests are developed, the existing information is checked and adjustments of age estimates are made to conform to the latest finding.

The study of position of rocks does not tell the age of rocks in number of years, but it does give information as to which rocks are the older in a given region. For example, if one examines a road cut in which the rocks are sedimentary in origin, and are in rather level, horizontal layers, he may assume that the rocks nearest the surfaces are younger than those in the next layer beneath them and that the rocks on the bottom are the oldest of the exposed rocks. Many children will be able to understand this relation between age and position of rocks.

If the rocks examined are folded, bent, or broken, and show signs of much erosion, the picture is no longer a clear-cut one. A person who has studied geology and who has studied the region in which the rocks are observed would be needed to determine which are the oldest rocks.

There are other ways of determining the age of rocks—including the "fossil indicator" method, the carbon method, and the lead method. These are not suitable for children, although they may be interested in knowing that such methods exist.

SOILS AND EROSION

Experience S-1. To observe soils in one's immediate surroundings

The purpose of this experience is to make children aware of the soil, and to lead them to notice that not all soils look the same. The method used in observation will vary with the location of the school and the policy of the school regarding field trips.

If you are teaching in a school where a field trip to observe soils is practical, you may wish to make the first exploratory trip a group experience. Unless your school is located in the heart of a large city, a walk around the school grounds and for an area of two blocks in all directions beyond the grounds should provide common observations on which to base discussions. Some of the things that might be observed on such a trip are: the color of the soil where plants are growing, the color of the soil where there are no plants, the presence or absence of sand, gravel or larger rocks, the thickness of the soil if there are places where this can be observed.

If you are teaching in a school where it is not practical to take the group to observe soil, perhaps individual children can make observations and tell the class what they saw. A brief class discussion of some of the things that might be observed would help individual children to know what to look for.

This experience may be used to help develop children's concepts

Soils and Erosion

related to the variety of soils that are present on the earth. It may also help children to have a better understanding of the interrelationships which exist between plants and soil.

Experience S-2. To study what is in soil

Find a place where permission can be secured to dig up all the soil in an area twelve inches square and six inches deep. Dig up the soil and put all of it in a pan or box. Be sure to get all of the living things that were in this soil.

Carefully begin to separate the soil. This may be done outdoors if there is a suitable place. If work is done indoors, newspapers spread out on a table or floor will make a good place to work. Then as the soil is examined it can be spread out. If a hand lens is available, the children will be able to see some of the smaller things more clearly. Keep a list of everything that is found. Not all soils have the same kinds of things in them. Frequently, in addition to the grains of sand or clay particles one can see parts of decaying plant leaves, stems, or roots, parts of animal bodies, larva or pupa of insects, adult insects, earthworms, spiders, and other small animals.

When all have finished looking at the soil, unless there is a good purpose apparent to the children, be sure to put it back in the place from which it was taken. If the soil is not returned, some of the animals in it may die. Also, if the hole is left in the ground, the next rain may cause erosion to start. Even when the soil is returned, the area should be covered by leaves and twigs. These will help to hold the soil in place until plants can grow over it. Try to leave the place with the least possible damage to the environment.

Experience S-3. To make a mixture as nearly like soil as possible

Several rocks and a container in which to mix soil materials will be needed. Hold two of the rocks above the container and rub them together. The result of the rubbing is similar to the result of the action of wind that carries sand as it blows against rocks, or the result of water that carries sand as it flows over rocks and as it rolls rocks against rocks. In all these cases rock particles are being broken into smaller pieces. Continue to work with the rocks until there is enough sand-like material to form the base for a mixture. If children have difficulty in breaking up their rocks, they may need to ask an adult for help. Frequently the school custodian will assist in such work.

Try to find some decaying leaves, stems, or roots. Break these up into very small pieces and add them to the rock materials. If any dead insects like crickets, grasshoppers, cockroaches and the like can be found, break them into small pieces and add them to the mixture. What living things should be added to the mixture? Earthworms would help to mix the materials. They would also help to get air through the soil as well as help with drainage. Do not put living things in the mixture unless they will be given a fair chance to live.

Does the mixture look very much like soil? Probably not. It is not possible to make real soil, for in addition to the rocks, animals, and plant life mixed together, real soil has been formed by the action of these things in a given climate, at a given elevation, and through a given period of time.

From this experience children may be helped to see the importance of saving soil, since even with hard work one is not able to begin with raw materials and quickly make good soil. The soil on the earth was formed during many millions of years, and once soil is gone it cannot be replaced easily or in a short time. Some soil scientists have estimated that between two hundred and a thousand years or more are required to build a single inch of topsoil from the raw materials of subsoil, depending on climatic conditions and the nature of the subsoil material. It would be far easier to work daily to build our soil than it will be to wait until all the top soil is gone and then start to work. The immensity of the problem is shown in this passage from Bennett:

> Available measurements indicate that more than three billion tons of solid material are washed out of the fields and pastures of America every year. This amount is enough to load a freight train that would encircle the earth eighteen times at the equator.[2]

Men who have worked on this problem are able to help landowners to build up their land following scientific methods.

Experience S-4. To find which soil material will hold the most water

Small amounts of sand, clay and humus, four empty tin cans of the same size, and four pieces of double-thickness cheese cloth, each

[2] Hugh Hammond Bennett, *Elements of Soil Conservation*, 2nd ed. (New York: McGraw-Hill Book Co., 1955), p. 15.

large enough to fit well over the end of the can being used, will be needed. Cut the tops and bottoms out of the cans. Tie a piece of cheese cloth over the bottom of each can. Put equal amounts, about two-thirds of a can, of each sample, sand, clay, and humus, in separate cans. Mix one-fourth can of sand, one-fourth can of clay, and one-fourth can of humus together and fill the fourth can two-thirds full with this mixture.

Secure four containers that will hold water and that are larger around than the tin cans already suggested for the samples. Support each of the cans containing samples over one of the larger containers. Pour equal amounts of water into each top can. Measure the amount of water that has run through each sample after five, fifteen, and thirty minutes.

Water will filter through the more porous samples first. The rate at which the water will flow through soils is important in helping to determine the kind of plants that will grow best in a given region. This information about the porosity of soils is also important to those who study ground water. (Only that water beneath the land surface which occurs where all pores in the containing rock materials are saturated is "ground water." The top of this saturated area is the approximate location of the "water table.")

Experience S-5. To observe the movement of water in cloth

Secure a tumbler or jar of water. Wet a piece of cloth and put one end in the container of water and the other end in an empty container. Notice how the water moves up through the cloth and drips into the dry container. In open-weave materials, such as cheese cloth or gauze, the action is more rapid than in closely woven cloth. If the containers are placed side by side, the movement of the water should continue until the level of water in the two containers becomes the same. You and the children will want to think about the relationship between this experience and the one which follows.

Experience S-6. To observe the results of the movement of water in soil

Fill a flower pot with dry soil and place it in a pan of water. Several hours later observe the pan of water. Is there less water in the pan? When much or all of the water is gone from the pan, pour the soil out on a newspaper or into a dry pan. Is the soil more moist than when it was put in the flower pot? It should be. However, if only a small amount of water was used, most of it may have been taken up by the pot. The soil might show little moisture. If this happens, add more water and let stand for a longer time.

Another way to show movement of water is to fill a glass tumbler with sand. Put a piece of cardboard over the top of the tumbler and invert it in a dish or pan. Carefully remove the cardboard so as to leave an almost full tumbler of sand inverted in a dish. Now pour a small amount of water in the dish. The water should rise, moistening the sand. More water may be added until all of the sand becomes wet.

Allow a potted coleus plant or any plant that grows well when watered from the bottom to become dry enough for the leaves to begin to droop. Then put the potted plant in a container of water. Observe the difference in the appearance of the plant in a short time. The water moves from the container of water into the soil. From the soil the water is taken up by the roots of the plant.

Water will be found to move easily through closely packed soil. Children may have had the experience of stepping on wet soil and seeing water come into the depression left by a footstep. This is one reason why it is desirable to have the surface of the soil loosened. Moisture does not rise so readily to the surface and, therefore, less is lost by evaporation into the air.

Some children may need help to see the relation between the movement of water in the cloth, in experience S-5 above, and the movement of water in soil, in experience S-6 above. More mature children may see this relationship after having these experiences.

Experience S-7. To test soils for acidity or alkalinity

Experiments carried out by those working in agriculture show that some plants grow better in slightly acid soil and others grow best in soil that is slightly alkaline. For this reason many workers have searched for a simple test that would show the amount of acid in a given soil. Most of the tests now in use in the soil-testing laboratories are not suitable for use by laymen, but one that has been used for many, many years is to test the soil with litmus paper.

To do this take a small sample of moist soil and press a strip of red litmus paper on it. If the paper turns blue, the soil contains more alkali than acid. If it remains red, it contains more acid than alkali, or the paper may be too old, or the soil may not be moist enough. In this case you may wish to do further testing.

If you are teaching in an area where much work is being done in soil conservation, some of the children may know and be able to demonstrate other ways of testing the acidity of soils. One of the more commonly used methods depends upon mixing soil and an indicator solution. After the soil settles, the solution is then matched with standard solutions of known acidity.

Experience S-8. To test different samples of soil to see in which a given kind of plant will grow best

If you do not live or teach in an area where samples of different kinds of soil can be obtained from landowners, you may be able to buy small quantities of soils from a florist. For samples of poorer soils you may find that the soil which has been used over and over again in flower pots for the same kind of plant will serve the purpose.

Small containers will be needed for your planting. These may be small tin cans, small flower pots, paper cups, milk cartons with the tops cut off, or any other small container that has holes, or in which holes can be made to provide for drainage. Into each container put about three inches of soil.

The kind of seeds used will depend upon the interest of the children. Vegetable or flower seed that usually grow in the area may be used. Different kinds of grass seed may be used, or perhaps seeds from some of the less desirable plants, weeds, that grow in the area.

Some of each kind of seed used should be planted in each kind of soil. Try to keep all of the containers at about the same temperature, and with as equal moisture as possible. When the plants begin to grow, try to see that all of them get about the same amount of sunlight.

As the plants grow there should be a difference in the growth of a given kind of plant in the different soils. Are there any containers in which no plants grow? If so, they might be replanted with more of the same kind of seed. Usually not all the seed of a plant will grow. Good seed may not have been used the first time.

Information of this type about the kind of soil in which a given plant will grow best is useful to farmers, gardeners, and soil conservationists. They use this information to help them decide which plants to use in order to get the best yield and to do the least damage to the soil.

Children may find this experience helpful in deciding what to plant in their home or school garden.

It might be well to work with children at this time to help them understand that doing an experiment once with a limited number of seeds is not enough evidence on which to base definite conclusions. But it does give them an indication of what might be expected if the test is repeated or the results used to indicate what seeds should be planted in their garden.

Experience S-9. To look for evidence of erosion in one's surroundings

If your school is one in which it is possible to take field trips, you will find this is another experience that lends itself to group study outside the classroom. If you are not permitted to take children outside the classroom, the children can still learn much about erosion in their surroundings. In either case you will probably need to talk with the children to find out their concept of the word *erosion* and to help them learn the correct meaning of the term.

You may find that many children use the word *erosion* to mean both weathering and erosion. With small children you may not wish to use both terms, but older boys and girls may be helped to see the difference between erosion and weathering. The term *weathering* is applied to the forces which break up rocks. *Erosion* is a term used for the transporting of soil, rocks, and weathered rock particles from one place to another.

If you stay in the classroom, you may be able to see evidences of erosion from one or more windows in the room. Also, by talking with the children about erosion and showing them pictures of places where soils and rocks have been eroded, you will be able to help them learn what to look for. Then, on their way home from school or on any trip that they might take, they will be able to recognize signs of erosion. These experiences that the individual children have may be shared in class discussions. Those children who enjoy drawing may be encouraged to make drawings of what they have seen.

If the group should go on a trip together, then you can make sure that all children have an opportunity to see places where erosion is taking place. You may be able to have your discussions while out of doors or you may need to discuss what you have seen after your return to the classroom.

Experience S-10. To observe differences in eroded and non-eroded areas

This experience can best be done by actually observing differences in eroded and non-eroded areas. However, if this is impractical, pictures showing a region before and after erosion can be used to make this a meaningful experience. Children need to become conscious of the changes that take place when soil is being eroded. They should be able to see that in eroded areas there is little plant life growing; washes, ditches, or gullies are forming; and the top soil is almost or completely gone. By comparing areas that are not eroded with areas where erosion is taking place, children can begin to see some of the necessity for preventing and checking erosion.

Children living in urban areas may not have an opportunity to do anything about erosion but they may be able to observe erosion or the results of it in vacant lots and public parks. The observation of trees that have much of the soil washed away from their roots and others that are leaning or have fallen because water has washed away much of the soil in which they grew will help children to become conscious of the importance of soil to plants. City children are as dependent on the soil for their food as are children living in rural areas. And it will be both urban and rural children who as adults will help to make and carry out our conservation policies.

Experience S-11. To show that all material in an area is not weathered and eroded by water at the same rate

Many times after a heavy rain if you look closely at the bare ground, you will be able to see that more soil has been washed from some places than from others. In places where the soil contains rocks these will sometimes be observed resting on little pedestals of soil. If you are limited in the amount of work that you and your children can do away from the classroom, you may not be able to make first-hand observations of this phenomenon.

Whether or not differential weathering and erosion are observed in the natural environment, you may wish to help your children observe the process more closely. If so, plan to work outside on the grass if possible. Use a wide board, a large shallow pan, or the bottom of a dishpan on which to make your landscape. Let the children mix sand, clay, garden soil, and pebbles. Then add just enough water to hold this mass together and form it into a mound of hills and valleys on the board or pan. Ask one child to fill a watering can and hold it above the newly made landscape. A large can with many holes punched in the bottom or a sprinkler type watering can may be used. Encourage the children to notice and talk about what happens as the can is held close to the mound and then high above it, on one spot for several minutes and then moved around so that it is never in exactly the same place. The children should be able to see a difference in the speed with which some of the materials break from the mound and are washed away.

If you cannot work out of doors, this may be done in the classroom. It will be necessary to arrange for the water and solid materials to flow into some large container such as a dishpan or tub.

Perhaps your boys and girls will be able to think of variations of this experience which they would like to try. For example, they may propose to make their mound or landscape and let it dry for several days before completing the experience. When possible encourage them to try out their ideas.

Formations such as those observed in the Grand Canyon of the Colorado River, Bryce Canyon and Arches National Monument in Utah are the result of differential weathering and erosion by wind and water. If an electric fan can be secured, a group of your boys and girls may wish to see what effects a steady stream or varying stream of air may have on their mound or landscape. The outcome is usually less spectacular than that resulting from the use of water, but the results are frequently interesting. By modifying the experience in this way you can emphasize that both wind and water help to shape our landscape.

When these experiences are tied in closely with a study of natural formations they will contribute to children's concepts of change, variety, interrelationships, energy, and time.

Experience S-12. To show by experiment some of the ways in which rocks are weathered (broken up or disintegrated)

a. BY FRICTION. The friction caused by rubbing one rock against another will break particles from the rocks. The results are more gratifying if the rock used is sandstone or other rock from which small particles may be easily broken. Think how long it must take natural forces to wear away rocks.

In nature this process of breaking up rocks by friction is most easily observed in swiftly flowing streams. If you teach near a stream that has clear water, you may want to take your class for a walk down to the bank of the stream. Here children may be able to see rocks being moved along over the surfaces of larger rocks and against other rocks as they are carried on downstream. If the children look closely at the rocks along the bank and at the edge of the water, they will see that the rocks are rounded and smooth. These rocks are very different from the sharp-edged rocks that come from quarries or rock cliffs. The rocks in the stream bed have been smoothed by the rubbing action of the rocks and grains of sand that are carried along by the water. This action is greatly increased at flood times when there is much debris in the water and when the water is moving much faster than it normally flows.

The results of weathering by friction may also be observed in places where wind carrying sand has worn away rocks. Some of the weathering in Bryce Canyon National Park, Zion National Park, and many other areas has been due to wind. Perhaps the stones in a cemetery have been observed. Many of the older stones have been weathered by wind and to a lesser degree by water until the inscriptions are difficult to read. On some no words are now legible. By noting the dates it is possible to see which kinds of stones have weathered most rapidly. This might help children to see that not all stones are worn away at the same rate.

Men make use of this process of weathering by friction in using sand-blasting machines to clean stone buildings. In this process small grains of sand are blown against the stone at a high speed. The outer surface of the stone is thus worn away, revealing a cleaner surface. Thus men do in a short time what natural forces take a much longer time to do.

Another evidence of stone being worn away by friction can be seen on stone steps or door sills of some old buildings. In some old buildings the steps have worn so much that it has been necessary to replace them.

b. By freezing water. Children may or may not have seen the effects of freezing water in breaking rocks. But if they live in a rocky region where there are freezing temperatures at night or both day and night for part of the year, this may be something they have observed many times.

Water is one of the few substances which takes up more space when it freezes than when it is in liquid form. Thus when it rains and water is held in a crack in a rock and later freezes, the expansion of the water as it freezes will usually cause the crack to become slightly larger. Each time this happens the crack becomes larger and may in time become large enough to break the rock into two parts. This action may be slow or fast, depending on the kind of rock, the size of the crack, the amount of water it holds, and the frequency of the freezing and thawing.

To show how freezing water can break a bottle, fill a small bottle with water. Put the lid on. Wrap the bottle in a piece of paper and put it in the freezing unit of a refrigerator. The paper will make the bottle easier to remove. When the water has had time to freeze, remove the bottle and examine it. The bottle should be broken. It should be handled carefully. If a bottle with a cork top was used it may not break, but the cork may be pushed up. This difficulty can be corrected by using wire or string to tie the cork down. Then freeze the bottle again.

In some parts of the country where water pipes are not buried deep enough to prevent the water in them from freezing during very cold weather, the pipes may break. Damage can be avoided by cutting off the water and draining the pipes before the temperature goes much below freezing.

An experience that will help children see how some rocks hold water may be helpful. Get a piece of sandstone and a piece of smooth non-porous rock like flint or fine-grain granite. Let them soak in a pan of water for an hour or longer. Then pick up each and try to wipe it dry. The sandstone cannot be wiped dry. Time will be needed for the sandstone to dry out. The other rock may be wiped dry in a short time.

If there is a refrigerator available for use or if the temperature outside is below freezing, the following might be tried. Soak a porous rock like sandstone for several hours. Then remove it from the water, wrap it in a paper and freeze it either outdoors or in the freezing unit of a refrigerator.

The results of this experiment are unpredictable because much depends on the amount of water actually in the rock at the time it

Soils and Erosion 75

freezes. Sometimes when the water freezes it does break off parts of the rock.

c. BY GROWING PLANTS. Perhaps plants have been observed growing out of what looks like bare rock. Sometimes a seed falls in a crack or depression in a rock that contains a little soil. The seed may begin to grow, and as the roots begin to grow down, they frequently force the crack in the rock to become larger and larger. The force of growing roots may be very great.

Children might like to see how much force the growing roots of a lima bean have. Take two pieces of glass of equal size. If the children are not accustomed to handling glass, help them learn how to handle it so that there will be little danger of their getting cut fingers. Make two T-shaped pieces of wood. The thickness of the wood should be about

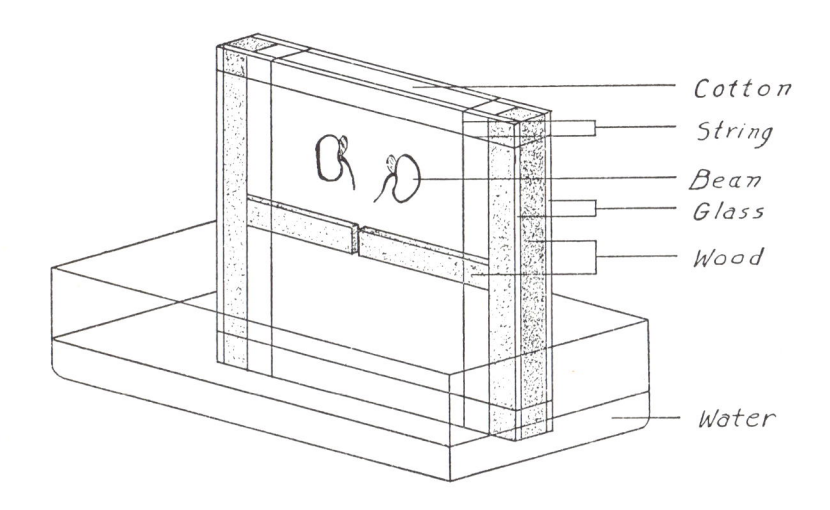

that of a soaked lima bean or whatever seed is being used. The top of the T should be the same length as the width of the glass. The bottom of the T should be long enough to reach from the end almost to the center. The space of about one-sixteenth inch should be left between the ends of the two T's. Cut a piece of blotter, paper towel or cotton slightly smaller than the glass plates and put it on the inside of the back glass. Now put two soaked lima beans on the blotter between the glass plates and above the bottom of the T's. Tie the glass plates together and stand them in a dish that contains a little water.

When the lima beans begin to grow, watch to see how the roots grow. Usually they will grow down between the ends of the two T's and either push them apart or push the glass plates apart.

d. BY RAPID HEATING AND COOLING. Rocks are sometimes weathered by rather sudden changes in temperature. The surface layers are usually the ones affected by temperature changes. It is thought that the rocky materials of some cliffs and mountains do not conduct heat very rapidly to the interior. But the outside layer of rock may undergo rather extreme changes in temperature. The temperature of a rock at night and its temperature when the sun is shining directly on it may be widely different. When the rock is heated, it expands. Then when it is cooled, it contracts. This change causes particles to break off from the surface of the rocks.

This action can be greatly speeded up in an experiment that can be done in the classroom. Any rock may be used. One containing a large amount of feldspar or quartz will usually give quicker results. Place the rock on a hot plate or other source of heat. Put a screen around the hot plate and rock as a protection against any small particle that may break off and fly out at an angle. After the rock has been heated for about an hour, quickly drop it into a container of cold water. Usually small particles from the surface of the rock will break off. Sometimes the entire rock may be broken with very little effort. This is frequently true if quartz is used.

e. BY CHEMICAL ACTION. Rocks are sometimes weathered by chemical action. Lichens, which are small plants that grow on otherwise bare rocks, produce chemicals which act to weaken the surface rock. As they grow, more of the rock is affected and particles become loosened from the rock. These rock particles, together with the dust and sand particles brought by the wind and caught around the lichens, help to build small amounts of soil. As this soil accumulates, more complex plants, usually mosses and ferns, may begin to grow on the rock.

If you teach in an area where there are rocks with lichens growing on them, you may be able to help the children see the soil particles that are being formed from the rock at the base of the lichens. It may be necessary to lift the edge of one plant in order to show what is happening to the rock. If this is done, the plant should be replaced when all are through looking. Also, it would be well to caution the children against scraping off all of the lichens they see. This is one of the natural ways of weathering, breaking up, rock.

Another chemical action takes place when water which is slightly acid flows over or through rocks. Some of the carbon dioxide in the air combines with water to make it a weak acid. The weathering caused by this acid is greater in limestone and marble than it is in most other kinds of rock. This chemical action has been largely responsible for many of the limestone caves found in this and other countries. Formations like the Natural Bridge near Lexington, Virginia, and sinks in Kentucky, northern Florida, and other limestone regions have been formed by the action of water that contains carbon dioxide.

If you live near one of the explored limestone caves, you may wish to go with the children on a guided tour through a part of the cave. Help children see the necessity for going into a cave only if adults are present, and only if it has been inspected and declared safe.

If part *b* of experience R-3, under *Rocks and Minerals*, was done, the action of a weak acid on limestone or marble was seen. Perhaps some members of the group would like to repeat this experience, or to do it for the first time.

Experience S-13. To show some of the factors which help to cause rapid soil erosion (transporting of particles from one place to another)

a. To compare the difference in the water run-off from a box of barren soil and a similar box of soil with grass growing in it. Almost any kind of box will do for this experiment. The kind in which grapes, cherries, tomatoes, or avocados come to grocery stores could be used. Cover the bottom and sides of each box with several thicknesses of newspaper so that the soil will not spill through the cracks. A burlap bag or other cloth could also be used for this purpose.

Fill each box to within one-fourth inch of the top with good soil. In one box, plant grass seed plentifully over the entire surface. It is desirable to get a rather thick growth of grass if possible. In the other box plant nothing. Put both boxes side by side where they will get some sun each day. Water both boxes as often as the grass needs it. If a spray to use in watering is not available, a satisfactory one can be made by punching many small holes in the bottom of a tin can.

When the grass is about two inches high you are ready for the next step.

Pull one end of the box of soil in which nothing is growing just over the edge of the table. Prop the other end up about one inch above the table. Put a large pan or other container just below the edge of the box extending over the table. Now measure one quart to one gallon of water, depending on the size of the box. Pour the water into the sprinkling can and move it around about six inches above the surface of the soil. Use all of the water as rapidly as it will flow through the can. Be sure to collect all of the water that flows off the box of soil. Pour this water and any soil that is in it into a glass jar.

Now repeat the process described in the previous paragraph, using the box with the grass growing in it. Use the same amount of water and spray it on as before. Again pour the water and any soil that ran off the box of grass into a glass jar the same size as the one used above.

After the water has stood long enough for all the soil particles to settle out, look at the two jars and notice the difference in the amount of soil in the bottom of each jar. Also notice whether there is a difference in the amount of water in each jar.

This experience should help to give the children some idea of the importance of plants in protecting soil against water erosion. It may also be used to show that much of the water falling on grass-covered soil is absorbed. This is basic to an understanding of one way to increase ground water reserves.

There are many variations of this experiment that may be done if time permits. Some of these are described below. The group may wish to plan and do other variations.

b. To TEST THE EFFECT OF ELEVATION ON THE ERODING EFFECT OF WATER FALLING ON BARE SOIL AND ON SOIL COVERED WITH GRASS. Use the boxes from *a* above. Prop one end of each box up four inches and repeat the experiment.

How do the results compare this time with those obtained earlier? There is probably a great deal more soil washed from each box, but still more from the barren soil. Erosion is usually more rapid on slopes than on level ground.

c. To COMPARE THE DIFFERENCE IN THE WATER RUN-OFF FROM GRASS PLANTED BY SCATTERING THE SEED, GRASS PLANTED IN VERTICAL ROWS, AND GRASS PLANTED IN HORIZONTAL ROWS. If the results for *a* and *b* above were kept, there will be no need to repeat the experiment for grass planted by scattering seed. Two other boxes of soil will be needed. In one plant grass seed in rows about one inch apart extending the length of the box. In the other plant grass seed in rows about one inch apart that extend from one side of the box to the other side. Thick rows of grass are wanted, but there should be no grass growing between the rows. When this grass is about two inches high, try the experiment of measuring water run-off as done in *a* and *b*.

How do the results differ from those for the box of grass where the seed were scattered? From those for the box of soil? Probably more soil was washed away from the box of grass planted in vertical rows than from the box of grass where the seed were scattered. How did the run-off from the box of grass that was planted in horizontal rows compare with the others?

This part of the experiment is to help show that wherever the soil is exposed to water it is more quickly eroded than if it is covered by plant growth.

d. To see the difference in the effect of wind on the erosion of barren soil, soil covered by grass, and soil only partly covered by grass. If *a*, *b*, and *c* of this experience were done, put the boxes where they will get some sun. Replace soil so as to fill the boxes again. Is the grass still growing? If not, replant the boxes as before, one in vertical rows, one in horizontal rows, and one with the seed scattered. When the grass is growing again, take the next steps.

Put the work table against a wall if possible. Spread paper so that it extends part of the way up on the wall and also under the edge of the box of soil on the table. Now place an electric fan about six feet away from the box and adjust it so that the breeze is directed onto the bare soil. Turn the fan on for five minutes. How much of the soil is now on the paper instead of in the box? Carefully collect this soil and put it in a glass jar.

Repeat the experiment, using the box of grass planted in vertical rows. Let the breeze blow down the rows. Collect and save the soil that is blown out of the box onto the paper.

Repeat the experiment, using the box of grass planted in horizontal rows. This time direct the breeze across the rows. Collect and save the soil blown from the box as before.

Repeat the experiment, using the box of grass planted by scattering the seed. Again collect the soil that is blown out of the box onto the paper.

Compare the soil collected from each of the four boxes. The soil blown from the box that was covered with grass should be less in quantity than that blown from the other three. The soil blown from the box with the grass planted in horizontal rows should be less than that blown from the box of grass planted in vertical rows. The most soil should have been blown from the box of barren soil.

Grass has been suggested in these experiments because it usually grows rapidly. Other kinds of plants might also be used.

Here, as in the experiments with water erosion, the children will be able to see the advantage of having plants growing in the soil to help protect it from wind erosion.

Children living in dust bowl areas have no doubt seen dust storms. They may learn from talking with their parents or soil conservationists how plants are being used to help check these dust storms.

Experience S-14. To observe areas where erosion has been checked

If you teach in an area where work is being done to check erosion, plan a trip with the children to visit some of these projects. If you cannot take the children to see examples of erosion control, pictures may be used to help them get an understanding of some of the things that are being done. Commercial pictures are always good, but frequently some one in the community may have pictures of erosion control in local regions which will be much more meaningful to the children.

Many men working in soil conservation will welcome an invitation to visit the school and share in your discussions.

Experience S-15. To make plans for checking erosion in an area children have observed

This is an experience which you and the children may not have an opportunity to carry out. But you might like to think through it together as a chance to review some of the things you have been doing.

Here are some of the things to be considered in making plans for checking erosion. (1) Will permission to work on the land be granted? (2) What kind of plants will be used? Plants that grow well in the climate, that have many roots to help hold the soil, and that have many leaves which help to cover the ground will be needed. What other things need to be considered in selecting the plants? (3) Will any kind of check dam be needed? If so, is there an adult in the community that could help to plan and build it? (4) Would this be a good place to plant one or more trees? If so, what kind? The kind of soil and the amount of water that will be available will need to be considered in selecting the right kinds of trees.[3]

FILMS ON ROCKS, MINERALS, SOIL, AND EROSION

You may find the following 16 mm. films a valuable supplement to your work in science.

Rocks and Minerals. 1954, 10 min., sound, black and white, and color. Film Associates, 10521 Santa Monica Blvd., Los Angeles 25, Calif. Illustrates the formation of igneous, sedimentary, and metamorphic rocks and suggests a few ways of grouping rocks.

Fossils are Interesting. 1956, 10 min., sound, black and white, and color. Film Associates, 10521 Santa Monica Blvd., Los Angeles 25, Calif. Introduces the concept of the earth's changing surface and changing life. Children find fossils and learn how fossils are used to help tell the story of the earth's past.

Birth of the Soil. 1948, 10 min., sound, color. Encyclopedia Britannica Films, Inc., 1150 Wilmette Ave., Wilmette, Ill. Shows how nature produces topsoil.

Understanding Our Earth: Soil. 1953, 10 min., sound, black and white, and color. Coronet Films, Coronet Bldg., Chicago 1. Deals with the soil profile, elements of soil, soil making, types of soil in United States, and the importance of conservation.

Learning Through Cooperative Planning. 1948, 20 min., sound, black and white. Bureau of Publications, Teachers College, Columbia University, 525 W. 120th Street, New York 27, N. Y. Shows a group of children studying erosion in some of the ways suggested in this chapter.

Erosion. 1951, 10 min., sound, black and white. Gateway Productions, Inc., 1859 Powell St., San Francisco 11, Calif. Primary film showing how the world is changing as a result of erosion.

[3] For a description of how upper elementary school children in one school beautified an eroded hillside, see Alice Miel and Associates, *Cooperative Procedures in Learning* (New York: Bureau of Publications, Teachers College, Columbia University, 1952), pp. 177-180.

Erosion. 1948, 6 min., sound, black and white. Government Films Dept., United World Films, Inc., 1445 Park Ave., New York 29, N. Y. The story of man-made soil erosion. Produced by the U. S. Dept. of Agriculture.

The Importance of Water. 1948, 10 min., sound, black and white, and color. Bailey Films, Inc., 6509 De Longpre Ave., Hollywood 28, Calif. Stimulates interest in conservation by presenting some specific projects and emphasizes the importance of the conservation of water and soil.

The River. 1939, 32 min., sound, black and white. Government Films Dept., United World Films, Inc., 1445 Park Ave., New York 29, N. Y. Traces the life in the Valley of the Mississippi River during the last 150 years. Produced by the U. S. Dept. of Agriculture.

CHAPTER FIVE

The Gaseous and Liquid Parts of the Earth

Air and water are part of a child's earliest experiences. During his prenatal development he is immersed in a liquid. And within the first eight hours after birth he is given water to drink and usually his body is cleansed with water. He must begin to breathe air immediately at birth. All through his life he continues to use air to breathe and water to drink and to keep his body clean. As he grows, he finds new uses for air and water.

When he is old enough to sit and play in his bath, he is frequently given toys. He observes for the first time that some things float in water and some do not. As yet he has no means of communication to tell us that his duck floats and his rabbit sinks, but nevertheless he is experiencing one of the properties of water. His concepts concerning water are growing. Later he finds that water mixed with soil is fun to play with, that it is fun to wade or swim in water, and, still later, that big boats are used to travel on water. These experiences help him to expand his concepts of water.

Many children have discovered through experience that some things when tossed into the air will float gently to the ground, that it is sometimes hard to close the door of a room or automobile if the windows are closed, that it is hard to pour a liquid into a narrow-mouth bottle, and many other common phenomena related to air.

By the time a child enters kindergarten or the first grade he has had many experiences with both air and water. His understanding and verbal knowledge of these two substances, however, will depend largely upon his adult contacts. Those children whose questions have been discussed with an informed, interested, and patient adult will usually have much to contribute to class discussions. On the other hand, those children who have not had this freedom of discussion at the level of their understanding may at first have little to contribute. Some may even have difficulty in asking questions, because the adult world to which they have been accustomed may be one in which the saying "Children should be seen and not heard" is practiced. These children should not be hurried into group participation. Nor should it be assumed that they are dull or uninterested. A classroom where one is free to express ideas, however poorly or inaccurately stated, without verbal or non-verbal disapproval; where one's questions and thoughts are given attention, but not necessarily agreed with; and where one feels free to request help and also free to say that help is not needed will encourage children to become actively participating group members.

There are many questions about the gaseous and liquid parts of the earth which children frequently ask. Information concerning these questions can be gained through reading and through adult help. In addition to these two sources of information, there are many experiences which children can have with air and water. Children should be led to realize that doing an experiment once does not prove anything. They need to learn early the value of repeating an experiment and also the value of checking to see if others get the same results. When results vary, repeating the experiment may help to explain why the results were not the same.

Through their experiences with air and water it is to be hoped that children will understand the importance of both of these to our healthy existence. If children have lived where the water supply has been inadequate, they may be able to contribute to a discussion of wise use of water. Children who live in areas where industrial waste is liberated into the air will have had first-hand experience with the disadvantages of polluted air. The pollution of both air and water is one of the nation's current problems. It is not likely to be completely solved before the boys and girls of today become responsible, voting citizens. Therefore, it is desirable to help them develop a feeling for the wise use of our air and water.

THE GASEOUS PART OF THE EARTH—
THE ATMOSPHERE (AIR)

The gaseous part of the earth is usually spoken of as the atmosphere, or simply the air. The atmosphere is made up of gases, water in different forms, and some solid particles. The proportions of most of these gases in the air remain relatively constant at all times for any given elevation. The amount of water vapor, carbon dioxide, and ozone in the air varies in different regions and at different times. The amount of dust, soot, bacteria, plant spores, plant pollen, and salts varies with both time and place. The atmosphere completely surrounds the solid and liquid parts of the earth and extends for an undetermined number of miles out beyond the surface. Some scientists think that there is some air in all of space. The density of the air is greatest near the land and water surfaces of the earth and decreases as one goes up away from these surfaces. It has been estimated that about half of the molecules of air are below and half are above three and six-tenths miles out from the solid and liquid parts of the earth.

This information about the atmosphere is the kind that children can do little about exploring for themselves. It has been included with the hope that it may be of help in answering some of the questions which children are likely to ask.

Experience A-1. To show that air is in many places

Children will have to accept the scientists' word that the solid and liquid parts of the earth are surrounded by a layer of air which is of undetermined depth. But each child can have experiences which will help him to understand more about where air is in his own immediate environment.

a. To find that all places where we can breathe contain air. Young children may find it interesting to check the presence of air by seeing if they can breathe in different places. They might check the area in a coat closet, in a box, in a big jar, near the floor, or (by climbing up on a ladder) near the ceiling. Thus children will have some experiences that will give meaning to the fact that on our earth air fills all spaces not occupied by something else. Be sure to caution children against climbing into places that close tightly. One needs only to put his head into a closet or a box to see if air is in it.

b. To show that air is in some places that seem empty. There are many things which we commonly speak of as being empty. Actually, most of these contain air. Children may be caused to think about this by being asked to find something in the room that is empty. Some of the objects collected may be used in the following experiences.

(1) *To show that air is in "empty" jars.* Float a cork in a pan or dish of water. Then take a jar of any kind that is "empty" and turn it upside down over the cork in the water. A cork is used to indicate the water level. What happened? The water came up only a very little distance into the jar. Then the jar must not have been empty. Something must be keeping the water out. Lift the jar straight up out of the water. Let the children feel to see that the inside of the jar, except around the opening, is dry.

They might like to crumple up a piece of paper or a handkerchief and push it down into the bottom of the jar. Now turn the jar upside down in the water. Be careful not to tilt the jar. Remove the jar by lifting it straight up. Wipe the mouth of the jar dry before you turn it over. Now remove the paper or handkerchief. Is it dry? It should be.

If this is an entirely new experience for the children, they may wish to repeat the experiment many times. There might also be an interest in trying out other jars or containers to see if they too are filled with air. This last step is important, for until it is done we can only say, "*This* jar is not empty." We would have no evidence that the statement might also be true of other jars. After trying out many jars we might conclude, "Many jars which look empty are filled with air."

(2) *To show that air is in "empty" boxes.* Take an "empty" pasteboard box such as a shoe box and cut a hole about one inch in diameter in the center of one end. Cut a piece of tissue paper one and one-fourth inches wide and long enough to extend from one inch above the top of the box to the bottom of the box. Cut the paper into narrow strips to within one inch of the top. Fold down the top one inch and place it over the top edge of the box above the hole. Put the lid on the box and press on the sides of the box. The paper strips covering the hole should be blown out as the air is forced out of the box.

Encourage the children to try other kinds of paper, and different lengths and widths of paper. Children might like to put their hand just in front of the hole when the sides are pressed. They will be able to feel the air as it comes out of the box.

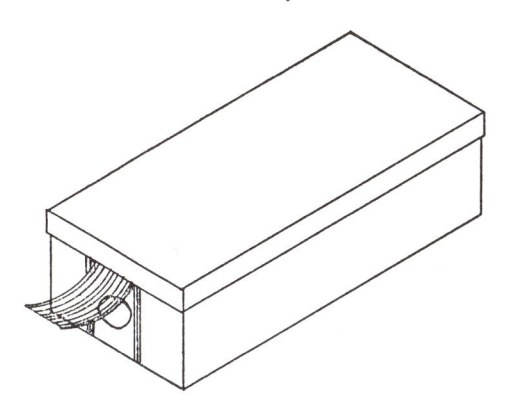

c. To show that air is in soil. For this experience any container of dry soil may be used. A small jar about three-fourths full of dry soil will do. Pour enough water into the jar to almost fill it, and look closely at the surface of the soil and the top of the water. You should see bubbles form at the surface of the soil and rise to the surface of the water. (This experience is sometimes more dramatic if the soil is put in a bottle with a narrow neck.)

Children may have had the experience of watering potted plants or garden plants and watching air bubbles come to the surface.

d. To show that air is in water. An easy way to show this is to fill a glass jar about one-half full of water and let it stand undisturbed for several hours. Look at the sides of the glass jar. You should see many tiny air bubbles. Shake the jar slightly and notice whether any of the bubbles rise to the surface.

Most people have learned to like the taste of water with air in it. Suggest to the children that at home they might let a tumbler of water stand over night. The next morning move the tumbler so that all of the air bubbles will rise to the top and burst. Then taste the water. It should taste different from the water that comes directly from the tap.

e. To show that air is in rocks. Rocks of any kind may be used in this experience, for almost all rocks have small air spaces in them. Fill a deep dish or pan with water and carefully drop several rocks into the water. If the surface of the rocks is observed closely, air bubbles should be seen coming from several places on the surface of the rocks.

Gradually the spaces within the rock that contain air will become filled with water and bubbles will no longer be seen rising to the surface. Sometimes small air bubbles will cling to the surface of the rock until they are jarred free.

Experience A-2. To find that things which are full of air cannot be filled with something else unless the air can get out

The material included in this concept may be used along with *b*, *c*, and *d* under experience A-1, above.

a. To FILL WITH WATER A JAR THAT IS FULL OF AIR. Turn a jar full of air upside down in a pan or other container of water. As long as the jar is held upright in the water the air cannot escape. Now tilt the jar slightly to one side. An air bubble comes to the surface. Hold the jar upright again. Notice that water has moved in to take the place of the air that escaped in the form of a bubble. Again tilt the jar. Notice that as more air bubbles leave the jar, more water enters the jar. When all the air is out of the jar, it will be full of water.

b. To FILL WITH WATER A MEDICINE DROPPER THAT IS FULL OF AIR. Hold a medicine dropper by the glass part and put the open end in water. Only a very small amount of water will rise in the tube, because the glass tube and rubber bulb are almost completely full of air.

Leave the open end of the medicine dropper in water and press the sides of the rubber bulb together. What happens? You should see many air bubbles come from the end of the glass tube and rise to the surface of the water. Release the rubber bulb. What happens? The glass tube and part of the bulb should be filled with water. Why? By pressing the sides of the rubber bulb together, much, but not all, of the air in the medicine dropper was forced out. Then when the bulb was released while the opening was under water, the water rushed in to fill the space where the air had been.

A hand plant spray, some of the children's water pistols, and fountain pens that use liquid ink work in much the same way as a medicine dropper. Also, a hollow rubber ball with a small hole in it can be used to show the principle that things full of air cannot be filled with something else unless the air can get out.

The Atmosphere

Experience A-3. To observe that air is lighter than water

Children have seen evidences that air is lighter than water, but they may never have thought about this. They have watched rain many times. But they may never have thought of rain as showing that water is heavier than air and can, therefore, fall through air.

Children of school age have also seen either oceans, lakes, or rivers. Ask them to think about the relative positions of air and water in the regions of oceans, lakes, or rivers. In each case the water rests on the solid part of the earth and the air is above the water.

Ask one of the children to invert a tumbler of air and submerge it in a container of water. Now if he tips the tumbler to one side, the air quickly comes to the surface. This shows that the air is lighter than the water.

Ask several children to hold containers of different sizes that are full of air. Now ask each to fill his container with water. Does each child notice a difference in the weight of the container he is holding? The difference should be quite apparent. Let the children empty their containers and exchange with someone else. Then repeat the experiment. Do they get the same results as before? In each case the container remained the same; the only difference was in the content. From these experiences it may be concluded that water is heavier than air.

If the children are given an opportunity, they will probably think of some of these and other ways of showing that air is lighter than water.

Experience A-4. To show that air can be put into some things

In some of our daily activities we make use of the fact that air can be put into some things. Most children will have had one or more of these suggested experiences.

a. TO PUT AIR INTO WATER. Fill a bottle one-half full of water and put a stopper in it. Shake the bottle vigorously. Now watch the little air bubbles come to the top of the water.

If frozen fruit juice is used at home, children may have noticed that the directions on the can usually say to stir or shake vigorously. This is to mix air into the juice. Most people think that this improves the flavor of the juice. If this is done, notice the "foam" on top. These are air bubbles that have risen to the surface but have not yet escaped into the air.

Those who cook frequently put air into different foods. Meringue, whipped cream, whipped jello, chiffon pies, many cakes, frostings, and many other foods have air beaten or folded into them.

b. To PUT AIR INTO SOAPY WATER. What causes soap bubbles? Put a little soapy water in a can or jar. Use a soda straw and blow some soap bubbles. Notice how round the bubbles are. Each bubble is air surrounded by a thin film of soapy water. The soap contains oil or fat which has a tendency to hold together. It can be stretched around a small amount of air. This makes the bubbles last longer than if water without soap was used. Look at the surface of the soap bubbles. Are there any colors similar to those seen when a drop of oil is put on water? Usually there will be such colors.

c. To PUT AIR INTO A PAPER BAG. Take a paper bag of any size and open it up. Now almost close the mouth of the bag by holding it about an inch from the opening. Spread the crumpled edges out and blow into the small opening. When the bag is full of air, close the opening completely. The paper bag is now full of air.

d. To PUT AIR INTO A BALLOON, INNER TUBE, OR BALL BLADDER. This is an experience which children usually have before they come to school. However, it is one which would bear repetition when attention is called to what is being done. If possible, a number of small balloons should be secured so that many children may take part in the activity. Allow children to experiment with putting air into the balloons and also letting the air out.

If you are working with young children who have not inflated balloons before, be sure that they blow out and remove the balloon from their mouth if they inhale through the mouth. Accidents have occurred where a child sucked air and a balloon down into his throat.

If an inner tube and a tire pump, or rubber balls with bladders that need to be inflated, are available, they would provide good materials for individual or small-group exploration.

Experience A-5. To transfer air from one jar into another jar

Fill a small glass jar with water by tilting it to one side in a dish or pan of water. Call this jar A. When jar A is completely full of water, stand it inverted on the bottom of the pan. Take a similar glass jar that is full of air and invert it in the pan of water. This is jar B. Put the air out of jar B into jar A. To do this hold jar A upside down and above the edge of jar B. Tilt jar B so that the air bubbles which leave it are beneath jar A. As jar B is gradually turned right side up beneath jar A, the air replaces the water in A and the water replaces the air in B.

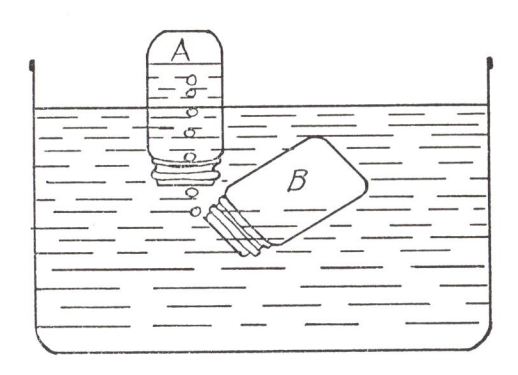

Without removing the jars from the pan of water see if air can be put back in jar B and water back in jar A. With a little practice children should be able to do this without difficulty.

If a place where children can work individually is available, it will be found that this experience is one which is fascinating to many children. They will repeat it many times.

Experience A-6. To practice a safe way to strike a match

Many children have been taught to be afraid of matches and fire rather than being taught how to use them with safety. Since adults do not often take time to teach children how to handle matches with safety, it might be time well spent to give children experiences with matches.

Secure several boxes of safety matches and a bucket of sand. Demonstrate a correct way of striking a match. The following is a suggested order of procedure: open the box, remove one match, close the box, hold the match firmly, strike it on the side of the box, move the match away from your body as you strike, hold the match as it burns so that the flame will be away from any part of the body, put the match out by one good blow on the flame, immerse the head of the match in sand for a few seconds and put the burned match in the waste basket. It might be well to show that water can be used for the same purpose as the sand, since it will be more available in homes.

After the demonstration of a correct way to strike matches, let each child who wishes to strike matches have the experience. Impress upon the children that an adult should be present when they use matches.

This is a time when it would be especially important to work closely with parents. They should know what is being done at school and what procedures are used. Then they will be better prepared to supervise the activity at home.

This is a specific case where intelligent understanding and manipulative ability can be substituted for curiosity and fear.

Experience A-7. To show that air (oxygen) is necessary for things to burn

Select five jars of different sizes and shapes. On each of six little blocks of wood, cardboard, asbestos, or glass fasten a birthday candle. Put the candles in a row. Behind each of the five candles place one of the jars. Have a bucket of sand handy and discuss how it will be used if needed. Light all six candles using correct procedures. At least two helpers will be needed. At a given signal five of the candles should be covered using the jars back of them. The sixth candle should remain uncovered.

As the children watch, the candles will go out one by one. The one in the smallest jar should go out first, then the candle in the next smallest jar should go out. Finally only the uncovered candle remains burning.

A group discussion might be used to bring out the idea that the amount of air in the bottle helps to determine how long the candle under each jar will burn. The candle not under a jar kept burning because it had much air available.

The children might like to repeat the experience. They might try using a different arrangement of jars. Or they might like to try other jars.

Experience A-8. To put out a fire by excluding air (oxygen)

Place several small pieces of wood in a metal pan set in a box of sand or on an asbestos mat put on a box of sand. Get a bucket of dirt

The Atmosphere

or sand. Now light the pieces of wood. Let the wood burn for a few minutes. Sprinkle sand on the burning wood. What happened? If all of the burning wood was covered; the fire was put out.

Empty the pan or asbestos mat and again put several small pieces of wood in the pan or on the mat. This time get a bucket of water. Again start the fire and let it burn for a few minutes. Pour water on the burning wood. What happened? The fire was put out.

Again set fire to some wood in the pan or on the asbestos mat. This time throw a folded towel, part of an old rug, a folded tow sack or any piece of closely woven fabric over the fire. Press it down quickly so as to cut off the air immediately. What happened? Again the fire was put out.

A fire has been put out using three different kinds of material. All of these methods of putting out a fire have one thing in common. Give the children a chance to try to figure out what it is. Small children may need some help. In each case air was excluded from the fire. Any method by which air is excluded from a burning object may be used to extinguish the fire.

This is an experience that can be made to have great practical value. But it also carries the potential for disaster if safety is not made one of the focal points of the experience. Talk with the children about why a metal pan or asbestos mat was used. These things do not burn. Discuss why the pan or mat was placed on sand. There are two reasons. One is to protect the table from the hot metal pan or mat. The other is to have an additional source of sand ready in the event that it might be needed.

If the children have not been taught how to strike matches, this experience will provide an ideal time for such an activity. See experience A-6 in this section for details on how this may be done. Be sure to observe this procedure whenever matches are used. It might be well when working with young children always to call this procedure to their attention. It is also highly desirable to have a bucket of sand close at hand whenever fire is being used.

If possible give children an opportunity to light and put out a fire under supervision. Let them satisfy their curiosity about fire under interested supervision. Each time be sure that all safety measures are taken. If there is uncertainty on the part of a child doing the experiment let him tell exactly what he is going to do before he lights the fire.

This is an experience which will take much time and may need to be repeated many times. It is one, however, which should do much to help change childish, impulsive action to thoughtful, deliberative action.

Experience A-9. To show that air contains different substances

Some children may never have thought much about air as a substance. They may be surprised when they first hear that air is made up of many substances.

a. TO SHOW THAT THERE IS WATER IN AIR. All of the children will have seen clouds and rain, and many will have seen snow, sleet, hail, and dew. But they may never have associated these phenomena with the statement, "There is water in air." Children can learn by doing some experiments as well as by observing natural phenomena that there is water in air. These experiences will provide an opportunity for children to expand their concepts of change. Here they will see that water may be changed to a gas or a solid.

(1) *To cause water to come out of the air.* Put ice in a metal cup. In a few minutes water should be visible on the outside of the cup. The amount of water on the outside of the cup will vary with the temperature and the humidity. The addition of salt to the ice may be used to make the reaction more visible.

If this is a new experience for the children, a worth-while discussion may follow the question, "Where did the water on the outside of the cup come from?" Let the children suggest ways of proving their statements. Carry out as many of these as possible. For example: if a child says the water comes from inside the cup, a child or the teacher may suggest that coloring the water in the cup would help to test this hypothesis. If then the cup is set in a white saucer so that the water which runs down the sides of the cup is collected, it will be found that the water in the saucer is clear. It could not have come from the colored water inside the cup.

The explanation of this phenomenon is based on the fact that warm air holds more moisture than cold air. When warm air comes in contact with the cold surface, the warm air is cooled. As the warm air cools, it can no longer hold as much moisture as when it was warm. Some of the moisture in the air is deposited on the surface of the cold object. The water on the outside of the cup of ice came from the air around the cup.

There are many variations of this experiment because of the many everyday experiences which involve this phenomenon. Class discussions may start in many different ways. If the group has lunch together where iced bottles or cartons of milk are served, the teacher may direct the children's attention to this phenomenon. Or children may ask questions about the water on the outside of their containers of milk. A discussion and related experiences may also follow: a child's account of drawing pictures on a window at home; a child's discovery of how his breath looks on a cold day; a child's observation of how his eyeglasses or those of a friend "cloud up" when he comes from a cold place into a warmer place; a child's account of seeing water collect and later turn to frost on the window panes in the kitchen while his mother is cooking. Sometimes the moisture will collect and run down from the top window pane and form icicles as it starts down on the lower window pane.

Often a discussion of water coming out of the air may easily be directed into a consideration of how water gets into the air. However, in many situations it is best to let the discussion of how water gets into the air wait until a later time.

(2) *To observe that water evaporates into the air.* Any type of open container such as a jar, saucer, cup, or pan may be used for this experience. Put some water in the container and note the water level. Place the container in a warm place and leave it undisturbed. By the next day there should be a definite lowering of the water level, or perhaps all of the water will be gone. The water has evaporated.

If this is a new experience for children, they may not at first be willing to accept that the water went into the air. They may insist that some one poured it out. This skepticism is a desirable attitude if not carried to extremes. We want children to feel free to question an activity they do not understand and suggest that it be repeated. Doing an experiment once does not prove anything. If such questioning is present, let the children suggest ways they could be sure that the water was not poured out. Encourage them to repeat the activity.

Attention may be called to the drying of wet clothes hung outdoors, the evaporation of water from sidewalks, roofs, and puddles, after a rain, and the evaporation from lakes, ponds, and oceans. This will help children to have some idea of where all the water that falls as rain might have come from.

For additional experiences with evaporation, see parts *a*, *b*, *c*, and *d* of experience W-5, in the section on Water.

(3) *To make a small cloud.* In a study of water in the air you may wish to help children see that many clouds contain water particles. Some children may have seen dust clouds and some may know that some of the very high clouds contain ice crystals. One way to make a small cloud is to heat some water and pour in into a milk bottle. Then pour out all but about one inch of the hot water. Hold some ice at the mouth of the bottle. A cloud will form when the warm air in the bottle meets the cold air near the ice. A piece of cheesecloth or other thin cloth stretched over the mouth of the bottle and tied will make a good holder for crushed ice or ice cubes.

If the weather is cold enough, ice will not be needed. While the water in the bottle is still quite hot set the bottle out in the cold. A cloud will be formed when the hot vapor above the water meets the cold air and condenses.

When water is boiled in a teakettle, a cloud can also be observed to form just beyond the spout. The clear area nearest the spout is steam. If this is done in school, be sure to caution the children about putting their hands in the steam. Steam is very hot and will cause a bad burn. Children may pass their hands through the cloud to see how damp it is. Or better, they may hold a saucer or tin cup in the cloud and observe the moisture which collects on it.

You may wish to try another method of making a cloud. If so, secure a glass gallon jug. Pour about one-half cup of water into the jug. Shake the jug so the water will come into contact with the air. Now pour out the water. Next light a match and hold it inside the jug. When the flame goes out remove the match. Check to see that the mouth of the jug is not hot. Blow your breath as hard as you can into the jug. Try not to let any escape. Then take the jug away from your mouth and a cloud should quickly form in the jug.

In this experience you have made sure there was moisture in the air in the jug. The burning match added tiny particles around which moisture could condense. When you blew into the jug you increased the pressure. This caused the air to be heated. When you removed the jar from your mouth you released the pressure and the air became cooler. As the air cooled it gave up some of the moisture it was holding. This moisture condensed around the tiny particles of dust and smoke in the air and became visible.

(4) *To observe that water comes out of the air.* Water comes out of the air in several different forms. Rain and dew are perhaps the most common forms. However, for children who live where it is cold most of the year, snow may be more common than rain. Moisture also leaves the air in the form of sleet or hail.

You may wish to talk with the children about the different forms in which moisture leaves the air and then together observe and discuss these natural phenomena when they occur.

If you are teaching children from rural communities, you may find that they are very conscious of dew. Such children are often up and out of doors much earlier than children living in cities.

b. To DECREASE THE OXYGEN IN A JAR OF AIR BY BURNING A CANDLE IN IT. Light a birthday candle and let a drop or two of candle wax drop onto an asbestos mat or a piece of glass or wood. Quickly stand the candle up in the soft candle wax. Let the candle burn a minute or two and then invert an empty jar over it. Observe that the candle burns for only a short time and then goes out. Why?

In order for anything to burn, oxygen must be present. When the amount of oxygen present in the jar becomes less than that needed for burning to take place, the candle goes out.

Formerly it was thought that all of the oxygen had been used up when the candle went out. Now, however, experiments have been done in which men in an airtight room were able to breathe after they could no longer get a cigarette to burn. This shows that there is enough oxygen left for human beings to breathe after a cigarette will no longer burn. According to this experiment, though, you would say that *some* of the oxygen has been used by the burning candle.

To continue the experiment, remove the jar and put it, opening down, on the table. Relight the candle. After it has burned for a minute or two, quickly put the jar down over it. Notice that the candle burns for a shorter time than it did at first. This process may be repeated several times.

Now remove all the air in the jar by filling it with water and pouring the water out. Shake or wipe the water out of the jar. Repeat the experiment. Does the candle burn for as long a time as it did at first? It should.

c. TO SHOW THAT WHEN A CANDLE BURNS, CARBON DIOXIDE IS GIVEN OFF INTO THE AIR. In order for this experiment to mean anything to children a test for carbon dioxide is needed which they can clearly see. The usual test is to hold a glowing splinter or a burning candle in the gas to be tested. If carbon dioxide is present, the splinter will stop burning and the candle will go out.

Another test for carbon dioxide is to mix the gas with clear lime water. Lime water is made by adding a tablespoon of calcium oxide, often called quicklime, burnt lime, or caustic lime, to one pint of water. The mixture should be made long enough before using to allow it to settle. The clear liquid above the white solid is used for the test. When this liquid is mixed with carbon dioxide, it should turn a milky color.

The test which gives the best results should be used.

Suspend a candle in a milk bottle or jar by coiling one end of a wire around the candle and fastening the other end of the wire to the under side of the cover of the container. Light the candle and cover the jar. The candle burns for a short time and then goes out.

If lime water is used to test for the presence of carbon dioxide, pour in about one-fourth cup of clear lime water. Shake the jar so that the gas and the lime water will mix. The lime water should turn milky.

If a glowing splinter or lighted candle is being used in the test, quickly lower either into the jar or bottle. The candle should go out, and the splinter should glow less brightly or go out.

d. TO SHOW THAT HUMAN BEINGS EXHALE CARBON DIOXIDE INTO THE AIR AS THEY BREATHE. Pour about one inch of lime water into a tumbler or small jar. Using a soda straw, let a child blow into the lime water until it begins to turn milky. This indicates the presence of carbon dioxide in the gases we exhale.

e. TO OBSERVE DUST IN THE AIR. If your school yard has an area of uncovered sand or loose soil, children may be able to observe the picking up of sand or dust when the wind blows. In some areas during a hot, dry season, dust is present in the air much of the time in quantities large enough to be clearly visible.

The Atmosphere

To see just how much dust there is in the air in the room, pull down the shades and using a strong flash-light or lantern slide machine direct a beam of light across the room. Probably dust particles that were not visible earlier can be seen. Sometimes a shaft of sunlight across a part of the room will also make dust particles visible.

f. To show that plant spores may be in the air. Perhaps the easiest way to show that there may be plant spores in the air is to grow bread mold. Bread mold reproduces from spores, which are usually present in the air. Whenever spores of this mold collect on suitable food that is warm and moist, they usually grow.

Children can grow bread mold in the classroom or at home. To do so they should moisten a piece of bread and put it in a saucer. Set the saucer in a place where it is warm and dark. Keep the bread slightly moist.

In a few days, signs of a mold should appear. As the mold grows, examine it with a hand lens. Small, round, black balls will grow on little stalks. These balls contain the tiny spores. If one is pressed between the fingers a black powdery material will be seen. These are the spores. The spores will be carried about by the air, and if they settle where conditions are favorable, they will grow.

Bread mold will also grow on sweet potatoes, grapes, tomatoes, plums, peaches, cherries, muskmelon, and strawberries. Children might like to have a mold garden using some of these foods.

Experience A-10. To observe that moving air has great force and can lift heavy objects

If you live in an area that has frequent wind storms, the children will be able to make or to recall observations of the wind moving objects. It is not uncommon in severe wind storms for houses to be destroyed or occasionally to be lifted by the wind, carried a short distance, and deposited again. Trees may be uprooted, roofs of buildings may be lifted off, and farm animals may sometimes be carried short distances.

In lesser wind storms one may see shingles removed from a roof, stone cornices blown from the tops of buildings, people blown down or occasionally picked up and carried short distances.

Observations in nature of the force of moving air should be made from a safe place, such as a well-constructed building.

If an electric fan can be obtained, it can be used to direct a stream of moving air. The force of this moving air on an object will depend on the size and speed of the fan and the nearness of the object to the fan.

Caution: Do not use a fan without a guard on it and be careful that children's hands do not get too close to the blades.

Test the force of the wind by holding pieces of paper in the path of the moving air. Vary the size of the paper and find out how large a piece of paper can be carried by the wind. Try both flat and crumpled pieces of paper. Also try balloons, small pieces of cloth, cardboard, and wood, and other light objects to see how far they will be carried by the wind.

Experience A-11. To show that air can be used to lift books or other weights

Get a large paper bag. Fix the opening so a stream of air can be directed into it and at the same time keep air from escaping. Put a book on the paper bag. Now, blow air into the bag. Does the book go up a little way in the air? It should.

Let the air out of the bag. Put on a second book. Blow air into the bag. Are both books lifted? Probably the answer is yes. Continue to repeat this, adding more books until the weight of the books is greater than the lifting force of the air in the bag.

Some of the children might like to repeat this experiment using a plastic bag, a balloon, or a ball bladder in the place of the paper bag.

Experience A-12. To show that air holds some things up and retards their rate of falling

Sometimes people make use of the fact that air tends to retard the falling of objects through it. Children use this in their play with balloons, paper, light-weight wooden gliders, and parachutes. But they may never have stopped to think much about why these objects float downward slowly.

a. TO SHOW THAT IF TWO PIECES OF PAPER OF EQUAL SIZE ARE DROPPED FROM THE SAME HEIGHT, THE ONE WITH THE GREATER SURFACE EXPOSED TO THE AIR WILL FALL MORE SLOWLY. Take two pieces of paper, each about 8½ by 11 inches. Crumple up one and leave the other flat. Let a child stand on a stool or chair that is protected with newspaper

The Atmosphere

and hold the pieces of paper out in front of him at as near the same level as possible. Ask him to drop both pieces of paper at the same time. Which piece of paper reached the floor first?

The crumpled one should. Why? Because more air was pressing on the flat piece of paper than on the crumpled piece. This helped to keep the flat piece in the air for a longer time.

b. TO MAKE AND USE A SIMPLE PARACHUTE. Take a piece of cloth about fifteen inches square. Cut four pieces of string fifteen inches long. Tie each string to a different corner of the cloth. Tie all of the strings together near their free ends. Fasten a small wooden block to the free ends of the string.

Put a paper on a chair and ask one of the children to stand on it. Let him hold the center of the parachute, straighten out the strings and then drop the parachute. The wooden block should fall slowly to the floor. If it falls too rapidly, the block is probably too heavy for the size of the parachute used. Use either a larger piece of cloth or a smaller block.

Try the parachute outdoors. Fold the cloth by holding the center and rolling it toward the strings. Then wrap the strings around the cloth. Now toss the rolled parachute as high into the air as possible. Did it unfold and the block float slowly down? If not, try it again. Sometimes a little practice helps. The strings often get twisted and keep the parachute from opening.

Paratroopers, whose real parachutes are very large and have many cords, learn to fold their parachutes so that they will always open. If the children are sufficienty interested in real parachutes, it may be possible to get someone from the community who can demonstrate how a real parachute is folded and how it works.

c. TO OBSERVE BALLOONS FILLED WITH AIR OR GASES LIGHTER THAN AIR. Blow up a balloon and tie the opening so that the air cannot escape. Let the children toss the balloon around, noting how little effort is needed to keep it in the air.

If possible, fill a balloon or two with natural gas. These balloons will float up to the ceiling if threads are not tied to them.

Children may have an opportunity to observe balloons used by the Armed Forces or the smaller balloons sometimes used for local advertising. The commercial balloons and dirigibles are inflated with helium. Hydrogen is lighter but burns readily, so the somewhat heavier nonflammable helium is used.

d. To show that air pressure is decreased in a stream of air. The science of aviation makes use of the fact that the air pressure in a stream of air is lower than the pressure just around it. If a stream of air is directed above an object, the air pressure above the object is lessened and the object will tend to be forced upward by the normal air pressure on its other surfaces.

Almost all children are interested in airplanes. They frequently can tell about the speed, number of engines, and characteristic shape of several different planes. They may be interested in learning a little about how airplanes stay in flight.

(1) *To decrease pressure over a strip of paper.* Cut a strip of writing paper or newspaper two inches wide and about eight inches long. Hold one end of the paper between your thumb and forefinger and let the rest of the paper hang down over the back of your hand. Hold your forefinger just below your mouth and blow over the top of the paper. What happens?

The paper should stand almost straight out on a level with the forefinger. If it does not, try using a lighter piece of paper or blow a little harder. Some children might like to experiment with different kinds of paper, with different lengths of paper, and with different widths of paper.

Why was the paper lifted when you blew across the top of it? Your blowing created an air stream above the paper in which there was low pressure. The normal pressure from below the paper forced it up.

(2) *To decrease pressure under a folded strip of paper.* Cut a piece of paper four inches long and two and one-half inches wide. Fold under one-half inch at each end. Place the paper near the center of a closed book or other stiff, flat object so that only the folded down ends touch the book. Hold the book so that you can direct a stream of air just over the cover of the book and under the folded paper. Blow hard. What happens?

The paper should bend down in the center. If you blow hard enough and direct the stream of air only under the paper, it will bend down enough to touch the book. You have decreased the air pressure beneath the paper and the pressure of the air from above forced the paper down. When you stop blowing, the paper should come back to its original position.

(3) *To decrease pressure between two ping-pong balls.* Suspend two ping-pong balls so that they hang side by side and about an inch apart. Scotch tape may be used to fasten a thread to the surface of a ball. Direct a stream of air between the two balls. What happened? The two balls should hit each other.

The pressure between them was made less than that on the outside. The pressure of the air on the outside of the balls was great enough to cause them to swing together.

You might like to try two small balloons in the place of the balls. If you can work where there is little or no wind current, you should get the same results as with the balls.

Experience A-13. To show that air exerts pressure

Children will have to read or be told how much pressure the air exerts (air pressure at sea level and 0° C. is 14.7 pounds per square inch), but they can do many things that show air exerts pressure.

You might wish to start this discussion by asking if anyone has gone to the top of a tall building in a fast express elevator, traveled in the mountains, taken an airplane ride, or been through a tunnel deep under ground or under water. Children who have had one or more of these experiences have been subject to rather quick changes in air pressure. Many of them will recall that their ears were affected. They may also recall that they were told to chew gum, or to keep their mouth open and to swallow frequently. These things help to change the air pressure in the middle ear so that it becomes the same as the air pressure in the outer ear.

With young children you may wish them to be conscious only that they have been where air pressure was changed rapidly. With older children you may find that they are more interested in how their body reacts. They may want to know more about the ear and its parts.

a. To feel the pressure of air against a moving object. Secure a piece of cardboard about 8½ by 11 inches or larger, and another piece about one-fourth the size of the large piece. Hold one piece of cardboard in each hand and move them quickly through the air. Cards should be held so that their greatest surface is toward the direction of movement. Is there any difference in the ease with which the two pieces of cardboard can be moved through the air? As was probably expected, the smaller piece was the easier to move.

Turn the pieces of cardboard edgewise and move them through the air. Now, of course, they are both much easier to move.

The children may want to carry out a variation of this experience the next time they go out on the playground. Cut the side out of a big cardboard box. If possible, use a box that is almost as tall as the children. Select two children who can run equally fast to work together. Let one hold the cardboard out in front of him and the other hold nothing. Now have a race. Who won? Probably the child not holding the cardboard. Why? Because the air exerted so much pressure against the cardboard that the child carrying it could not run very fast. Let the other child hold the cardboard and have the race over again. Perhaps others would like to try. (If cardboard is not easily available, open out several pages of a newspaper and use them.)

b. To observe the effect of the pressure of moving air against a pinwheel. A simple pinwheel may be made by cutting a square of paper any size. A five inch square might be a good size to start with. Draw lines from all four corners to the center. Cut on these lines to within one-fourth inch of the center. Fold every other point to the center. Let them overlap slightly and push a pin through these four points and the center. Stick the pin in the eraser of a pencil.

Hold the pencil that the pinwheel is fastened to in one hand and move it quickly forward. Notice how the pressure of the air caused the pinwheel to spin. Hold the pinwheel and blow into it.

If pinwheels are new to the children, they may like to run with them on the playground.

Pinwheels of different sizes may be made, from the same kind of paper, and put side by side in the wind. Is there any difference in the speed of the large pinwheel and the small one? There probably is. Since more surface is exposed to the air in the large one, it will require more pressure to turn it. It has more resistance. If the pressure is the same on both pinwheels, then the small one should move faster than the large one.

The Atmosphere

c. To show that water will rise in a bottle if part of the air is forced out and the bottle inverted in a pan of water. There are different ways of forcing some of the air out of a bottle. One effective way is to replace some of the air with hot air. Put water in a teakettle, being careful not to fill it above the spout. This is so there will be a chance for the steam to come out of the spout.

When steam is coming from the teakettle spout, invert a milk bottle over the spout. Leave it for about a minute. Hold the bottle with a towel and remove it from the spout. Quickly lower it, mouth down, into a pan of water. As the hot air in the bottle cools, the water will rise in the bottle.

The reason is that the steam from the teakettle will replace much of the air in the bottle and warm any of the air that remained in the bottle. Then when the warm air cools there is less pressure in the bottle because warm air occupies more space than cold air. The air pressure on the water in the pan is greater than that in the bottle and forces water to rise in the bottle. Water will rise until the pressure inside the bottle is equal to that on the outside.

If a heat-resistant bottle such as a nursing bottle is available, another way of showing this same phenomenon may be tried. Invert the air-filled nursing bottle in a pan of water. Pour hot water over the outside of the bottle. Look closely at the mouth of the bottle. Air bubbles should be seen escaping. Continue to pour hot water over the bottle until few air bubbles can be seen. Now be patient and watch the bottle. As the bottle cools, water will rise in it.

Here again the air pressure has been decreased in the bottle by removing some of the air. Water will rise in the bottle until the air pressure inside the bottle is equal to the pressure on the surface of the water in the pan.

d. To use air pressure to make a fountain in a bottle. Change the cool air in a milk bottle or nursing bottle to hot air as is suggested in part *c* of this experience. Take a ball of clay. Flatten it until it is about one-half inch thick and larger than the mouth of the bottle. Cut a soda straw in half. Put half of the straw through the clay. Take the bottle that contains hot air and quickly cover the opening with the clay. The straw should extend about half way up in the bottle. Then quickly invert the bottle in a pan of water. Be sure to hold the bottle so that the clay and the open end of the straw are above the bottom of the pan. As the bottle cools water will shoot up through the straw, forming a fountain inside the bottle.

If clay is not available, anything may be used into which a straw can be sealed leaving both ends open, and which will prevent water from entering the bottle in any way except through the straw.

e. To show that air pressure is necessary if one is to drink through a straw. Most little children learn to drink through a straw, but few know that air pressure helps them in any way.

Fill an empty milk carton or milk bottle two-thirds full of water. Put a soda straw through the bottle cap or top of the carton and let it extend down about one inch below the surface of the water. With a candle seal the straw in position. Also seal around the bottle cap or any opening left in the top of the carton. Now try to drink the water. Any success? Very little, unless there is a leak somewhere. Why? Because there is no air pressure to force the water up.

Try this again without sealing the straw in and with plenty of space for air to enter the bottle or carton. Now when the air is drawn out of the straw the water comes up in the mouth. When the mouth is removed from the straw, the water stops. Why? Air is pressing down on the water in the bottle or carton. But the water can't come up in the straw, because the straw is full of air and the pressure on the water is not great enough to force the air out. When the air is removed from the straw by sucking on it, then the air pressure on the water is strong enough to force the water up. As long as air is kept from entering the straw the water will flow until it is all gone.

f. To show that air pressure helps us to pour liquids out of a narrow-mouth bottle or jug. Fill a narrow-mouth bottle with water and turn it upside down to pour the water out. What happens? Probably a little water comes out and then an air bubble must make its way up through the water to the bottom of the bottle. Then some more water will come out and again stop. More air goes up. As the bottle gets more air in it, the water will come out more quickly and more evenly. Holding the bottle on its side and gradually increasing the angle at which it is inclined will help to let air in at the top of the opening and water out at the bottom, thus producing a steady stream.

g. To show that air pressure helps us to pour liquids out of a can. Perhaps the children have poured fruit juice or milk out of a can, or they may have seen a filling station attendant open a can of oil. How many holes were punched in the top of the can? Two? What happens if only one hole is used? The children might try it the next time they open a can of milk or fruit juice.

If there is a jar with a screw top, let it substitute for a can. Using a can opener or a nail, make one opening in the jar top. Fill the jar with water. Screw the top down tight. Turn the jar upside down. What happens? Not much, if any, liquid comes out.

Turn the jar on its side with the hole at the bottom. Turn the jar on its side with the hole at the top, at the side. Still no water will come out. Hold the jar upside down and shake it. What happens? A little air bubble goes in as a drop of water comes out. But that takes a lot of effort, and it is hard to direct the water into a tumbler or other jar.

Put another hole in the top opposite the first hole. Now turn the jar upside down. What! No water. Hold the jar on its side with the holes at equal distance from the floor. Still no water. Try holding the jar on its side with one hole above the other. Water? Yes, a nice steady flow.

What has been found out? That any time air cannot enter a container, such as a full can or jar of liquid, the liquid will not flow out. But any time that air can enter, as it does through the top hole when the jar with two openings is turned so that one hole is above the other, the liquid will flow.

People not only use this principle in opening cans of liquids, but they have made use of it in the type of drinking fountain where there is a large bottle of water inverted on top, in spigot type thermos jugs, and in some types of animal watering bottles.

h. To show that air presses on a card with enough force to keep water in a tumbler. Fill a tumbler to the brim with water. Put a card or piece of slick-surfaced paper over the mouth of the tumbler and turn it upside down. The card or paper should extend out beyond the edge of the tumbler from one-half to two inches. Be sure to hold the card on tight while turning the tumbler so that no air enters the tumbler. Take the hand away from the card. The air is pressing up on the card with enough force to hold the water in the tumbler. Be sure to do this over a pan or sink, because as the card or paper becomes water-soaked, air begins to enter the tumbler, water is forced out, and the card soon drops.

Try filling the tumbler one-half full of water, hold a piece of paper over the opening, and invert the tumbler. Hold the paper until the water fills the lower one-half of the tumbler and the air fills the upper half. Usually the paper will hold until it becomes soaked. Repeat the experiment, using less water each time until the smallest amount of water that can be held in the tumbler by the air pressing on the card is reached. At this point, the water plus the air in the tumbler exerts just a little less pressure on the card than the air outside the tumbler is exerting on the card.

Children may have trouble holding the card against the mouth of the tumbler so that no air enters it. They can be helped by giving them a small piece of wood or stiff cardboard to put over the card. Then as the tumbler is inverted they can hold the card flat against the tumbler. The block can then be removed.

i. TO SHOW HOW A SIPHON WORKS. A rubber or flexible plastic tube will be needed for this. Perhaps one of the children can find a bath spray that is ready to be discarded and can salvage the tube. If not, small lengths of rubber tubing can usually be bought at drug stores or hardware stores. Flexible plastic tubing can usually be bought where aquarium supplies are sold. Take a jar, can, or bucket and fill it almost full of water. Put this container on a table. Call it A. Take another container of about the same size and put it on the floor beneath A, and call it B. How can the water be transferred from A into B by using the rubber tube? Try putting one end of the tube in the water in A and let the other end hang down toward B. Nothing happens! Why? The tube is full of air and the water cannot enter.

Replace the air in the tube by forcing water through the tube. This may be done by holding the tube in a U shape and pouring water into one end of the U until water flows out the other end. Now hold a finger over each opening, and put one end below the water in container A and hold the other end at a lower level than the first and direct it toward the empty container B. Remove both fingers from over the openings. The water will flow untill all the water is gone from A

The Atmosphere

or until the upper end comes above the water and air goes into the tube.

Before the siphon stops, lift B above A, being sure to hold the tube beneath the water surface in each container. The water will flow back into A.

Note: Another way to remove the air from a siphon is to put one end of the tube below water or whatever liquid is being siphoned and with the mouth or other suction device, draw the air out. There is a disadvantage in using the mouth if the water and the tube are not clean, for one is likely to get a mouthful of dirty water. As the air comes out, the liquid takes its place and will flow until all the liquid is gone or until air enters the tube again. This method seems least desirable for use with children, since many will want to use the siphon and since it is difficult to sterilize the tube.

This is another way to fill the tube. Put the entire tube below the surface of the water. Take hold of one end and move it around in a circular fashion until all the air is out. Then, while holding both ends beneath the surface of the water, put a finger over one opening. Remove the end with the finger over it while keeping the other end below the surface of the water. Hold the end of the tube that has been removed below the level of the first and remove the finger. This is an easy method once a person learns to keep both ends of the tube beneath the surface of the water while filling the tube.

j. To show that air pressure can be used to pick up small objects from the bottom of an aquarium. If children have learned how to work a siphon, they are ready to put it to use. If they do not know how to use a siphon, it would be desirable for them to do *i* above.

Fill a siphon tube with water and insert one end in the aquarium and the other at a lower level directed into a container that will hold water. When the siphon is flowing, carefully and slowly move the end of the tube along over the surface of the bottom of the aquarium. Waste materials will be drawn into the tube. Practice will show how close to the sand the tube can be held to get the waste and not the sand. It is best to collect this waste in a container that can be examined for snails or other small animal or plant life which should not be removed. Accidents may happen even after much experience with this method of cleaning off the surface of the sand in an aquarium.

k. TO SHOW THAT SUCTION CUPS WORK BECAUSE OF AIR PRESSURE. Suction cups can usually be bought at five-and-ten-cent stores and hardware stores. Sometimes single cups are used to hold coat hangers. Towel racks and soap trays are sometimes equipped with suction cups.

In using a suction cup, the inside surface of the cup is moistened and then the cup is pressed against a smooth, flat surface. When the cup is pressed in, some of the air inside the cup is forced out. The water helps to seal the edge of the cup so that no air can enter when the cup is released. If air can be heard to rush in, the cup will not hold. Try again. If the cup holds at first, it will remain tight until the edge is loosened and air is allowed to enter the cup.

Air pressure on the inside has been decreased so that the pressure on the outside is greater. This increased outside pressure will help to hold the suction cup in position.

l. TO SEE THE EFFECT OF A GREAT DEAL OF AIR PRESSURE IN RESISTING FORCE. Secure a piece of wood about one-eighth of an inch thick, one inch to three inches wide, and about eighteen inches long. A thin slat from a fruit crate usually works successfully. If materials are to be bought, ask for laths.

Put the wood flat on a table or desk. Let about four inches extend over the edge of the table. Open up three large sheets of newspaper and lay them over the wood. Be sure the paper comes to the edge of the table and that the wood is near the center of the paper rather than far to one side. Smooth out the paper so that it will lie flat with a minimum of air underneath it. Then with your hand or the side of the head of a hammer, strike sharply the wood that extends beyond the table. If all goes well, the wood will break. If it does not break, check back to be sure all steps were carefully followed.

Why does the wood break? The air pressure on the paper is so great that the wood is held down to the table. When the wood is struck, it cannot lift the paper and therefore must break.

If there is some question about the weight of the paper, an equal amount of paper may be crumpled and balanced on the wood. Now strike the end that extends over the table. The paper and stick will both fly up. It is not the weight of the paper that holds the stick down but the air pressure on the paper.

Caution: Be sure that children do not stand too close to the table while this experiment is being done, because the stick sometimes flies up.

m. To determine the approximate amount of air pressure being exerted on the paper in part l above. At sea level and 0° C., air presses with a force of 14.7 pounds on every square inch of surface. For practical use we often consider it 15 pounds per square inch.

Measure in inches the length and width of your opened-up newspaper. Multiply these two figures together and you have the number of square inches on the surface of the newspaper. Now multiply this number of square inches by fifteen and you will have the approximate number of pounds of air pressure on the newspaper (approximately eleven thousand).

n. To make a simple barometer. If you save the large pieces of broken balloons, this is the place to use a piece of rubber. Stretch a piece of rubber balloon over the mouth of a milk bottle and tie it down securely. With glue fasten a soda straw to the rubber so that one end reaches the exact center of the rubber. Hold or put a weight on the straw until the glue dries. Fasten a pin, pointed end out, in the other end of the straw.

Take a small piece of white paper and make black lines across it one-eighth of an inch apart. Find a place to put the milk bottle near a wall where it will be undisturbed, but where the pointer can easily be seen. Put the marked paper on the wall so that the pointer comes to rest at about the center mark. When the air pressure increases, there is increased pressure on the upper surface of the rubber. This causes the rubber to move down in the center, forcing the pointer to move up. When the air pressure decreases, there is less pressure on the upper surface of the rubber. The rubber then moves up, forcing the pointer to move down.

o. To show that when air pressure in a can is decreased, the air pressure outside the can will be great enough to cause the sides of the can to be bent in. Secure an empty can with one opening that can be closed completely with a cork or cap. The can may be a quart, half-gallon, or gallon size. Some brands of insect spray, varnish, liquid wax, antifreeze, turpentine, and many other products come in suitable cans.

If the can is small, put one-half cup of water in it and set it on an electric hot plate. If a larger can is being used, one cup of water may be put in it. Be sure to leave the opening uncovered. When the water is boiling and steam is coming from the opening, remove the can from the hot plate and quickly seal it with a stopper or cap. Let the can rest on an asbestos mat and observe it as it cools.

Soon a noise should be heard and one side of the can will be seen bending in. As the cooling continues the can may become quite bent in and topple over.

What has happened? Part of the air in the can was forced out by the steam as the water boiled. The can was then sealed so no air could enter it. As it cooled, the steam in the can turned back to water. This reduced the pressure inside the can. The pressure outside the can was strong enough to cause the can to partially collapse.

Caution: Be sure that the can is not covered while it is being heated.

p. TO SHOW THAT AIR PRESSURE CAN BE USED TO PUT A HARD-COOKED EGG IN A BOTTLE, AND ALSO TO TAKE THE EGG OUT OF THE BOTTLE. Boil an egg until it is hard. Let it cool and remove the shell. Select a quart milk bottle with as large an opening as can be found. Take a small piece of paper about three inches square. Fold the paper several times. Hold one end of the paper and light the other end. As soon as it is burning, drop the paper into the milk bottle and put the egg, small end down, on the mouth of the bottle. If this is done quickly enough, the egg will bounce up and down several times and then suddenly slide into the bottle.

What happened? The hot air caused by the burning paper forced out some of the air. The hot air escaped by forcing the egg up; the egg then dropped down. The pressure became greater in the bottle and forced the egg up again. Some air escaped and the egg dropped down again. When the burning paper went out, the air in the bottle began to cool. It had less pressure. The pressure on the outside was then greater and it forced the egg into the bottle.

To get the egg out, increase the pressure inside the bottle. Rinse the burned paper out of the bottle and wash off the mouth of the bottle. Empty all the water out and get the egg small end first into the neck of the bottle. Put your mouth against the opening of the bot-

The Atmosphere

tle and direct a stream of air up one side of the egg. Lower the bottle from the mouth and catch the egg as it slides out.

There are other ways to put an egg into a bottle and to take it out again. In all cases the principle is to reduce the air pressure inside the bottle when putting the egg in. Then increase the air pressure inside the bottle when the egg is to be removed.

The air pressure in the bottle may be decreased by inverting the bottle over the spout of a steaming teakettle. After about one minute remove the bottle and put the egg on the mouth of the bottle. As the bottle cools the egg should slide into it. This is a little cleaner way, but requires a little more time since the water must be boiling.

Try removing the egg by using hot water. Invert the bottle with the egg in the neck. Hold the bottle with tongs and pour hot water over the bottle. As the air in the bottle is heated, it expands. The pressure inside the bottle is increased, and the egg comes slowly out of the bottle.

A suitable substitute for the egg in this experiment was described in a class at Teachers College, Columbia, in the spring of 1954, by Patrick Corsentino. Put enough water in a small balloon to cause the balloon to be about the size and shape of an egg. Then tie the neck of the balloon. The remaining procedure is the same as that followed when using an egg. For many this will be cheaper than using eggs. It also has the advantage of being easily adapted to whatever size bottle opening is available.

Experience A-14. To observe that hot air is lighter than cold air

Use a yardstick, dowel rod or other lightweight stick about a yard long. Secure two paper bags of the same size. Open them up and fasten a short string to the center of the bottom of each bag. Fasten one bag to each end of the stick. Suspend the stick so that the bags are exactly balanced and free to move. Hold a lighted candle under one bag. What happened? The bag with the cold air is heavier and moved down. This pulled the bag of hot air up.

Remove the candle. Wait a few minutes and then hold the candle under the other bag. As the air in this bag is heated, it expands. Some of the air escapes through the open end of the bag. The content of the bag is now lighter than the full bag of cooler air and is pulled up.

Heat causes air to expand. That is, heat causes molecules to move more rapidly and to spread out so that they occupy more space. Thus for a given volume there will actually be fewer molecules of hot air than of cold air. The fewer the molecules, the less the weight.

Experience A-15. To observe that differences in temperature cause movement of air

It is differences in temperature that are responsible for most of the wind movements on the earth. Since almost all children have played outdoors on a windy day, they have had experience with moving air caused by temperature change. Children ask questions about the wind and where it comes from. This is one of many important phenomena which we experience and make use of. But we as adults often forget to question the causes of these or try to understand them, so that frequently we are not willing to think through and discuss children's questions. By our words or tone of voice we often give children the feeling that they should not ask questions about such natural phenomena.

The following experiences should help to give a better understanding of winds.

a. TO SHOW THAT AIR EXPANDS WHEN HEATED. If *c* and *d* of experience A-13 have been done, evidence was observed which showed that air expands when heated. The following are other ways to show that when air is heated it expands.

(1) *To inflate a balloon by heating air in a bottle.* Use a nursing bottle that can be heated. While the bottle is at room temperature and filled only with air, stretch a *small* balloon over its opening. The balloon will hang limp over the side of the bottle. Heat the air in the bottle by standing it in a pan or dish of hot water or by holding the bottle just above a hot plate and turning it slowly.

As the air is heated, it expands. The balloon is slowly inflated. Allow the bottle and the air in it to cool. The cool air takes up less space than the hot air, and the balloon will again hang limp over the edge of the bottle. If the bottle is then put in ice water, the air continues to contract. The balloon may be forced into the bottle by the air pressure outside the bottle which is thus greater than the pressure inside.

(2) *To feel a balloon expand as the air in it is heated.* Inflate a balloon until it is about one-half to three-fourths the size it could be. Tie

The Atmosphere

the opening so that air cannot escape. Hold the balloon about eight inches above a hot radiator or hot plate and rotate it in the hands. Soon the balloon can be felt to expand. As the air inside the balloon is heated, it expands. Move the balloon away from the heat and feel how it changes.

This change in size of the balloon may also be observed by watching closely as the balloon is heated.

If possible, provide an opportunity for all children who would like to have this experience. Actually only the person with both hands around the balloon has good evidence that the air is expanding.

(3) *To measure the expansion of a balloon that has been heated.* Find a tumbler, water goblet, or jar and partially inflate a balloon until it will just go inside the mouth of the container. Put the container about two feet from the hot plate. Heat the balloon by rotating it in the hands about eight inches above the hot plate. After the balloon expands, quickly lay the balloon on the mouth of the container. If this can be done before the air in the balloon begins to cool, the balloon will no longer go down into the container.

Note: If the top of the container is the least bit rough, or if it is desirable for the top to be more visible so that the amount of expansion can be more easily seen, put adhesive tape around it. To do a smooth job, put the tape around the top, letting about half of the tape extend above the container. Now cut the tape at inch intervals. Next fold the tape down an inch at a time.

b. TO SHOW THAT AIR CONTRACTS WHEN COOLED. Put a small amount of air into a balloon and tie the opening so that the air cannot escape. Notice that there are few if any wrinkles in the rubber. Immerse the balloon in a pan of ice cubes and let it remain for several minutes. When the balloon is removed, there should be a visible increase in the number of wrinkles in the rubber.

An even greater contrast can be shown by repeating (3) above. After showing that the heated balloon will not go into the container, cool the balloon in a pan of ice cubes. When the balloon is put over the container this time, it should go inside rather easily.

c. TO SHOW THAT HOT AIR MOVES UP. That hot air moves up is one of the fundamental facts which are useful in the understanding of winds. (Actually hot air is pushed up by cold air that moves in under it; this is not clearly demonstrated in (1) and (2) below, but is shown in *d.*)

(1) *To observe that on a calm day smoke goes almost straight up.* If there are smoke stacks visible from the school grounds, a committee or the class might go out and make observations. It may be necessary, however, to work in the classroom. If so, make a damp paper torch that will smoke when it is lighted. A round lamp wick coated with petroleum jelly on one end might also be used as a source of smoke. Light the coated end of the wick and let it burn for a few minutes. Put out the flame by blowing on it. Usually the wick will continue to burn slowly and give off much smoke. If the air in the room is undisturbed, the smoke will go straight up.

If the children have parents or adult friends that smoke, they may have observed how straight the smoke rises when the air is undisturbed.

(2) *To observe that air over a hot radiator is moving up.* Use a source of smoke such as a damp paper rolled up or a wick coated with petroleum jelly. Hold this over a hot radiator. The smoke should go straight up.

If you are working with small children, you may not want them to use fire. Let them make pinwheels or cut strips of thin paper and hold them above the hot radiator. The paper strips or pinwheels should move in a direction that indicates upward air currents. (See page 104 for directions for making a pinwheel.)

Other sources of heat may be substituted for the radiator. A hot plate, alcohol burner, candle, or gas burner may be used. Be careful in using any of these that the children do not get burned. Have a bucket of sand or water at hand in case the paper objects catch on fire. Before starting, review what each will do in case something does catch on fire.

d. TO SHOW CONVECTION CURRENTS IN A JAR OF AIR INVERTED OVER A BURNING WICK. Secure a gallon jar like the ones in which restaurants frequently get pickles, mayonnaise, peanut butter, and jam. Clean the jar thoroughly. Use a round wick and coat the end of it with petroleum jelly. Cut off about one-half inch of the wick and place it on an asbestos mat. Light the wick and, while it is burning, invert the jar over it. If a wick is not available, pieces of soft string about one-fourth inch long may be twisted together and coated with petroleum jelly.

The smoke should rise in a straight column to the bottom of the jar, move along the bottom, then down the sides of the jar, and toward the wick again. Why does it do this?

The burning wick heats the air above it. Hot air expands and is then lighter per unit of volume than cold air. Heavy cold air moves in under the warm air and forces it up. When the warm air strikes the cooler glass, the air is cooled. This air is now heavier and sinks to the bottom of the jar. Here it again moves in under the air being heated by the burning wick. The smoke is used to make the path of the air more visible.

These currents of air are similar to the ones that occur in nature. For example: soil is heated more rapidly during the day than is the water in an ocean or lake. The air above the soil during the day is therefore warmer than that above the ocean. The cool air from over the ocean moves in over the land and pushes up the warmer air. This accounts for breezes which blow in over land during the day.

Water loses its heat more slowly than land does. At night the air over the land cools more rapidly than that over large bodies of water. There are breezes which blow from the land out over the ocean. Again cool air is moving in under warm air and forcing it up.

THE LIQUID PART OF THE EARTH—THE WATER

You might like to begin a discussion of water by using a globe. The children would be able to see that a large part of our earth is covered by water. In fact, about three-fourths of the earth's surface is covered by water. Most of the water is in the large oceans which form a connecting system around the land masses.

The water in the oceans is rich in minerals that have been weathered and eroded from the land. Rivers that flow across the land masses of the earth carry this mineral wealth to the oceans. This abundance of minerals makes it possible for many kinds of plants and animals to live in these large bodies of water.

Children will have had experiences with rain, creeks, or rivers, and perhaps with lakes and oceans. They will also have had some experiences with the other states or forms in which water may occur. Water may exist in its three forms at room temperature. For example, you may drink a glass of liquid water with solid ice cubes in it and breathe air that contains water in a gaseous form.

In each of its forms water may be both helpful and harmful to people. We need liquid water to drink, to keep our bodies and clothes clean, to grow our food, and for many other purposes. But water as rain erodes the land, and may flood fields and destroy homes and business property. It may even destroy life. Ice cubes cool our drinks and ice helps us to preserve our food. But ice may block harbors and sink ocean liners. Snow may protect some plants and supply moisture to the soil, but it may also block highways and streets. Steam may be used to heat homes and other buildings. It may also be used as a source of power for many industries. But if it is improperly handled, it may be a very destructive force.

Although water is present on the earth in large amounts, there is a growing shortage of the water suited for many of man's uses. This shortage is largely the result of these many uses people have found for water, and of our extravagant or wasteful use of water. Much of the waste has resulted from a feeling that water is plentiful and cheap. One check on the use of water in cities where meters were used and in similar cities where meters were few shows the following results. In cities where 50 per cent or more of the users of water had meters, the average daily use was 52 gallons per person. In cities where only 10 per cent of the users of water had meters the average daily use was 128 gallons per person.[1] This was only a limited check, but it does reveal the tendency to use excessively or waste a product that is cheap and plentiful.

There are many places where water is not plentiful. In a few places on the earth, drinking water is available only every other day. In such places there is no water to use for baths or for washing clothes. We are fortunate in the United States to have had so much water so widely distributed. But our supply in many regions is decreasing. We need to learn ways to use our water supply more wisely.

Nearly all children have had fun playing with water. Many of them will have done some of the things suggested in the following experiences, but may never have given much thought to the activities. Children need experiences with water that will help them to learn

[1] Thomas King, *Water—Miracle of Nature* (New York: The Macmillan Co., 1953), p. 199.

about its characteristics. They also need to become conscious of its importance in our daily lives. It is hoped that the following experiences may contribute to these goals.

Experience W-1. To observe that water goes into some things and runs off of other things

Children usually like to play in water, and this experience will give them an excellent opportunity to combine play and learning. Fill a dishpan or bucket about one-half full of water. Let the children put many different things into the water. They will find that water goes into things like cloth, sponge, blotting paper, newspaper, unfinished wood, some rocks, and any other porous material which they have. When they put these things in water and then remove them, they feel wet and usually stay wet for some time.

If materials such as a clean glass tumbler, a new nail, a painted wooden block, a plastic toy and other non-porous materials are put in the water, the water will not go into them. When they are removed from the water, they can easily be wiped dry, or if they are allowed to stand, most of the water flows off them. If this experience is explored by older children, a discussion of one reason why wooden boats and houses are painted may be included.

Children may also observe that the feathers of some birds and the fur of some animals seem to shed water easily. Some children may have watched ducks in water and seen the water roll off their back feathers, and may have noticed that when a duck walks from the water onto the land it usually fluffs its feathers once and looks dry. Children may also be helped to discuss why it is that they go swimming without protecting their bodies from the water but that long distance swimmers need to protect their bodies by coating themselves with some form of oil. Perhaps some members of the group can think of substances other than their skin which do not absorb water quickly but that over a period of time will absorb some water.

Experience W-2. To show that some things float in water and others do not

This may be done as a part of the previous experience or it may be done independently. Put water in a bucket, pan, or other good-sized container. Let the children drop objects into the water and note which ones float and which ones sink. Be sure to try objects of the same material but of different sizes and shapes. Also try objects of the same size and shape made out of different materials, if any can be found.

Objects float if they displace water the weight of which is equal to or more than the weight of the object. If the weight of the water displaced is less than the weight of the object, the object will sink.

Put a sponge in water. It will float because it has many air spaces which cause it to be lighter than the water it displaces. Hold the sponge under water and squeeze it so that the air is replaced by water. Now put the sponge on top of the water. It will sink as soon as it is turned loose. Why? The water now in the sponge is heavier than the air it replaced. The sponge is now heavier than the water it displaces.

Similarly a solid steel ship will sink. But a ship made of steel with large air spaces in the hull will float.

Experience W-3. To show that things float higher in salt water than in fresh water

Float a small block of wood on a pan or bucket of water. Mark as accurately as possible the level of the water on the block. This may be done by carefully removing the block from the water and putting a pencil line right between the wet and dry part of the block.

Make a pan of salt water by adding about four level tablespoons of salt to a quart of water. Float the block on the salt water. It should float higher than it did in fresh water. If equal volumes of fresh water and salt water are weighed, the salt water will be the heavier. The same object will displace a greater weight of salt water than of fresh water even though the volume remains the same.

If it is difficult to get the block marked accurately, the following device might be made. Cut a soda straw so that there are two tubes of equal length. Make pencil marks on one piece of the straw at one-fourth inch intervals. Put a small ball of clay on one end of the straw. Put the clay end of the straw in a bottle of fresh water. Does it hold the straw so that part of it extends up out of the water? If not, add to or take off clay until the straw is held floating vertically with part of it extending out of the water. Note the number of markings showing above the water.

Transfer the clay and straw to a salt water solution and note the number of markings showing above the water. More markings should show above salt water than were visible above fresh water.

If children have been swimming in salt water, they know that it is easier to float in salt than in fresh water. People who swim in Great Salt Lake find that they float very easily in the water. Much more of their body is above water than when they float in fresh water.

Experience W-4. To show that water is taken up by air (evaporation)

See part *a* (2) of experience A-9 on the atmosphere, page 95.

Children should have this experience before going on with other experiences on evaporation. Children who have had the experience earlier may wish to repeat it now. It will serve as a review and a basis for further discussions.

Experience W-5. To show that the rate of evaporation is not always the same

Since the rate of evaporation depends on several things, it might be well to let children discover some of the things which affect this rate.

a. TO SHOW THAT TEMPERATURE AFFECTS THE RATE OF EVAPORATION. Try to find five jars, saucers, or dishes of the same size and shape. Into each let the children put an equal amount of water. Then select five places that vary in temperature where the five containers might be put. If the radiator is on, be sure to put one on or very near it. The others might be distributed as follows: one on the floor as far away from the source of heat in the room as possible; one on the tallest object in the room; one near a window; one on a desk or table near the center of the room. Try not to put any where wind will blow on it.

Notice and keep a record of the location of the dish in which all of the water evaporates first. The water in the container that was in the warmest place should evaporate first, and that in the coolest place should evaporate last. This is because, when other factors are constant, the water will evaporate faster when the temperature is higher.

b. TO SHOW THAT MOVING AIR INCREASES THE RATE OF EVAPORATION. If there is a chalkboard on which water can be used, this experiment can be done indoors. If not, perhaps the group can work outdoors on a sidewalk. Mark off two eighteen inch squares about six feet apart on the chalkboard, or on the sidewalk.

Ask three children to help. Give two of the children wet sponges or wet cloths. Ask them to wet the squares that have been marked off as soon as the starting signal is given. Give the third child a piece of cardboard that he can use as a fan. As soon as the two children have completed their job, ask the third child to fan one of the wet sections. The square that is fanned should dry more quickly than the other one. Moving air increases the rate of evaporation of water if other factors do not enter in.

The following is another way to show that moving air increases the rate of evaporation. Use two containers of the same size and shape. Put an equal amount of water in each. Locate two places of about equal temperature in the room. A thermometer may be used to check this, but it is not necessary. Carefully put the containers in place. On one direct an electric fan so that it will blow across the container but will not blow the water out. The water should evaporate first from the dish over which the fan is blowing.

c. To show that the surface area exposed to the air influences evaporation. Collect five containers with openings of different sizes. Place them together on a table. Into each let a child put the same amount of water. In which does the water evaporate first?

The container with the largest surface of water exposed to the air is the one from which the water should evaporate first.

d. To observe that the humidity, water already in the air, affects the rate of evaporation. It is necessary to know the temperature and the relative humidity. The relative humidity can be gotten from radio weather reports, newspapers, or a weather station. On a day when the humidity is high hang a wet towel up to dry. Record the temperature and the time it takes for the towel to become dry. On a day when the humidity is low and the temperature is about the same as on the day when the first part of the experiment was done, wet the same towel and hang it up to dry. Note the time it takes for the towel to become dry.

On which day did it take longer for the towel to dry? It should take longer on the day when the humidity is high.

To make the experiment more accurate, measure the amount of

water used to wet the towel. Then use the same amount each day the experiment is done. It will be necessary to experiment to find out how much water to use. Towels differ a great deal in the amount of water that they can hold.

It will probably be difficult to find two days in which the temperature and movement of air are the same and the difference in humidity great. But perhaps conditions will be such that the experiment will help children to see that humidity is a factor in evaporation.

You might like to check the effect of humidity on rate of evaporation in another way. On each of two days when the humidity is different, place the same amount of water in the same container and each day put it in the same place. Make a record of the time required for evaporation on each day.

Experience W-6. To show the relation between evaporation, cooling, and personal comfort

It might be well to help children see how the conditions which affect rate of evaporation also affect their comfort. A discussion in which children recall the difference in their feeling of comfort during various hot days might indicate where to start work. One or more of the following experiences might be helpful.

a. TO FEEL THE COOLING EFFECT OF RAPID EVAPORATION. Invite someone to help. Then wet one piece of absorbent cotton with water and another with rubbing alcohol. Ask the helper to extend both hands palms down. Moisten an area on the back of one hand with water and a similar area on the back of the other hand with rubbing alcohol. Which liquid evaporates first? The rubbing alcohol. Which hand felt cooler? The hand with the rubbing alcohol. In order for a liquid to evaporate heat is needed. In this case heat was taken from the hand as well as from the surrounding air. This is why the part of the hands where the alcohol and water were put felt cooler than other parts.

If possible provide a time when all children who wish may have this experience.

b. TO OBSERVE THAT MOVEMENT OF AIR ALONE DOES NOT CAUSE COOLING. Secure two thermometers and hang or stand them up in different places. After about twenty minutes record the temperature reading of each thermometer. Wait another ten minutes. Has the temperature changed in either location? Probably not. If for some reason the temperature in the room does seem to be changing, wait until this is not true before going on with the experience.

Now direct an electric fan so that it will blow on the bulb of one thermometer and not on the other. If no electric fan is available, let children take turns fanning the one thermometer. After ten minutes is there a change in the temperature? Check again after twenty minutes. There should be no change in temperature if the movement of air is the only condition that has been changed.

c. TO FEEL THE COOLING EFFECT WHEN MOVEMENT OF AIR IS USED TO SPEED UP EVAPORATION. Wet both hands with water. Hold one still and wave the other. Which hand feels cooler?

If it is a hot day one notices people fanning. Why? The movement of air does not cool. No, but the movement of air speeds up evaporation, and evaporation causes cooling.

d. TO OBSERVE THE COOLING EFFECT WHEN MOVEMENT OF AIR IS USED TO SPEED UP EVAPORATION. Hang two thermometers side by side and wait until the temperature readings are the same. Around the bulb of one thermometer wrap absorbent cotton. The cotton may be tied in place with thread. Wet the cotton thoroughly. Place an electric fan where it will blow on both thermometers. After a short time, do they still show the same temperature? The one with the wet cotton should show a lower temperature while the temperature of the other should remain the same. After the cotton dries, the temperature shown by the thermometer with the cotton should rise slowly.

An interesting variation of this experience might be as follows. Let both thermometers return to room temperature. Then wrap absorbent cotton around the bulb of the other thermometer. Wet the new piece of cotton with rubbing alcohol and the other with water. Again turn on the fan. Is there a difference in the temperature shown by the two thermometers? There should be.

These are more scientific ways of showing what was done in *a* and *c* above. That is, here the actual difference in temperature can be measured. In *a* and *c* one is dependent on the sensation of coolness, which will vary with different individuals as well as with the same individual at different times.

Water

Experience W-7. To show that water may be taken out of air

The concepts involved in this experience have been discussed earlier, in part *a* (1) of experience A-9, page 94. There the emphasis was on a study of the atmosphere and the substances contained in it. It is included here because the emphasis is on an understanding of water and its relationship to the atmosphere.

Experience W-8. To observe that water comes out of the air

This observation was discussed, in connection with the study of substances contained in air, in part *a* (4) of experience A-9, page 97. It helps children see that through natural causes some of the substances normally present in the atmosphere may separate from it. It is suggested here, however, to develop an important concept about water.

Experience W-9. To show that many things contain water

Experiences W-4, W-5, W-6, W-7 and W-8 deal with water in air. Water is also in many other things. Fruits and vegetables all contain water. Cut several fruits and vegetables and notice how juicy or watery they are. Put pieces of a potato or apple in a tin can and place the can on a hot plate. Place a saucer or piece of glass over the top of the can. Do you notice moisture beginning to collect on the saucer or glass? As the food is heated it loses some of its moisture. This moisture collects on the glass as water droplets. Try other fruits or vegetables.

Children may have had experience with powdered milk, condensed milk, or exaporated milk. These products have had all or part of the water removed. Prunes, raisins, dried apples, dried peaches are all foods that have had some water removed.

Animal tissues also contain water. Children should not be encouraged to find this out experimentally since it would mean the death of the animal. The learning involved is not usually considered important enough to justify taking the life of an animal. Children may, however, be encouraged to look at the meat their mothers prepare and to notice how moist it looks.

Sometimes meats have had most of the moisture taken out of them. This is true of dried beef, dried fish, and many cooked meats.

Jelly fish are animals with a high percentage of water in their bodies. They are about 95 to 98 per cent water.

Experience W-10. To become conscious that the care of public water is our responsibility

The extent of the work which you will want to do in this area depends a great deal on your community and the age of the group you are working with. The problem of an adequate water supply is so important, however, that people of all ages should work toward its solution.

Our technical knowledge concerning the proper disposal of waste materials makes the use of our lakes and rivers for such purposes a disgrace. We as adults are not meeting our social responsibility when we fail to work toward correcting such a problem. We as teachers of children need to help them get a feeling of responsibility for all parts of their environment.

Elementary school children should not be used to try to correct such a community problem. But they can be helped to observe conditions and to correct their own behavior. By their questions and interest they may act as the stimulus for adult action. Children can become useful helpers in a community project, but they should not spearhead such work. If the community is not yet ready for action, a change in the individual behavior of children with regard to waste disposal will nevertheless, in the long run, be worth the time spent in studying the problem.

These experiences will be found useful in helping children to expand their concepts of the interrelationships between themselves and their environment.

a. To observe that rivers and lakes may be contaminated. Take a trip to the nearest lake or river. Walk along its bank. Is the water clear and clean looking? Or are there papers, bottles, tin cans, and other debris on the bottom and along the bank? Is the water muddy? Is there indication that garbage or sewage has been emptied into the water? Has the state health department put up signs along the banks saying the water is polluted and must not be used?

Perhaps none of these things will be true. But the chances are that human beings have left ample evidence of their visits.

Ask the children to imagine what the bank and bed of the lake or river was like before waste was dumped into and on it. During such discussions several considerations should be brought out. One is aesthetic. Bodies of water and their surroundings may be beautiful, restful places to visit. Carelessness of individuals and a lack of information frequently make such places otherwise. Another important factor is that of health. Some disease-causing bacteria and other harmful organisms usually live in polluted water. Harmful bacteria, rats, mice, roaches, and ants may all live in litter along the banks. Water animals as a source of food should also be discussed. The kind and number of animals and plants living in any body of water are greatly affected by the amount and kind of waste dumped into the water. Few of the kinds of fish usually considered as food fish are found in polluted water. The few that survive are considered undesirable as a source of food. Shellfish are either killed or may become carriers of disease organisms. Usually only a few forms of scavengers can live in polluted water.

b. To show one way to clean water. Secure a tall can. One such as fruit juices come in would be good. Cut out the bottom. Over one end stretch three layers of cheesecloth and tie it so that it will not slip. Fill the can to within an inch of the top with clean sand. Support the can over a large container. Pour dirty water in the can. Be careful not to run it over. Keep pouring dirty water onto the sand. After a while look at the water that has come through the sand. It should be clear.

Some cities make use of sand filters in their water purification plants. The children might find out how their city purifies its water. The water that collects under deep beds of sand and may come to the surface as springs is usually quite clean and free of harmful bacteria.

Small quantities of water may be cleaned of most kinds of harmful bacteria by boiling for thirty minutes. This is not practical for city supplies. Chlorine is used by some cities to help purify their water.

c. To show that water can be stored. Water evaporates when it is exposed to the air. Therefore, if we wish to store it, a very effective method would be to exclude the air. Many cities do have closed water storage tanks. Some cities, however, use lakes or open reservoirs. In general, these are found where the needed stored water supply is very large.

One of the best places to store water is in natural underground storage places. Such storage places are not man-made, but people are learning how to increase the supply of water in them. They plant ground cover such as trees and grass that will help to hold the water and allow it time to sink into the underground reservoir. In some places people have built drainage channels into these underground storage places. These are used to divert rain water from rivers and hold it underground where it will be available for later use.

Some children may have heard people talk about the water table. This is the level of water in these underground storage places. In many places in North America the water table is being lowered.

To show the contrast between the amount of water that evaporates from a container exposed to the air and one that is closed, two containers of the same size will be needed. Be sure that one of them can be sealed. In them put equal amounts of water. Seal one container. Leave the other container uncovered. Put them away side by side where they will not be disturbed. There should be a visible difference in water level after the first day. Finally the open container will be empty and the other will contain as much water as it did at the beginning of the experiment.

d. TO OBSERVE THAT WATER IS ESSENTIAL TO CERTAIN TYPES OF RECREATION. This is rather obvious. Yet it might be worth while to show the relation of water supply to its use in recreation. Swimming is a recreation enjoyed by many children. Watching and listening to the play of water in a fountain can be very pleasurable recreation. In cities when there is a water shortage, pools and fountains are left dry. When the water in rivers and lakes is polluted, the state health department usually posts "No Swimming" signs.

The restrictions on swimming show children how they are affected by poor care of our water supply. There are other recreations in which water is necessary. Many children are interested in boating and canoeing, fishing, water skiing, and surfboard riding.

Visit swimming pools, boat docks, and fishing places if there is an opportunity. Note the condition of the water. Also note the number of people taking part in any of the activities. If the water was in better condition, would more people be able to take part in any of these activities?

Experience W-11. To show that some things dissolve in water and that others do not

Drop a lump of sugar and a colored glass marble into a tumbler of water. Watch what happens. Slowly the sugar disappears, but the marble remains unchanged. The sugar has dissolved in the water.

Water

Try such things as salt, sand, washing soda, sawdust and other things that are available. Children will find that many things dissolve in water, and some float on or in it.

The amount of a material that dissolves in water may be increased by heating the water.

Experience W-12. To show that when most water evaporates solid particles are left

Is there a teakettle available in which water has been boiled many times? If so, it might be well to start by examining the inside of the kettle. Usually there is a creamy white colored film coating the inside of a teakettle that has been used for some time. This is a deposit of minerals that have been left as the water evaporated in boiling. In some areas there are few minerals in the water and such a deposit may not be found except in kettles used for long periods of time.

Children might like to polish the inside of an aluminum saucepan and then boil water in it for an hour or longer. Let almost all of the water boil away. Is there a film of minerals left on the inside of the pan? Probably there is unless you are using mineral-free water.

Water from which all minerals have been removed is called distilled water. Children might like to boil some distilled water and note the lack of a mineral deposit.

Experience W-13. To show that running water has great force

Children living near rivers or who have seen rivers at flood stage will be able to add much to a discussion of this topic. Most children will have seen pictures of trees, houses, and other buildings being carried away by the force of running water.

Some may have seen evidence of the force of running water on a small scale. Sometimes after a hard rain one may observe rather large quantities of soil, rock, and debris being washed into a storm sewer.

That running water has force can also be shown in the following way. Take the largest container available and put in several inches of sand and gravel. Pour in water from a teakettle or hold under a faucet. Notice that the rocks and gravel are moved about. If the rate of flow is increased, there will be a greater movement of sand and gravel.

The above experience is not very spectacular. If children can work with a garden hose out on the school ground, they can get more dramatic results. Perhaps arrangements can be made with the school custodian for the children to watch the next time he waters the lawn and flower beds. Then they can observe how the water moves the soil and any small rocks that are present.

The discussion of this experience should be useful in helping children broaden their concepts of change and interrelationships.

Experience W-14. To show that water may be changed to a gas or a solid

The substance formed when two molecules of hydrogen combine with one molecule of oxygen may exist in three states. The liquid state is water. The gaseous state is steam. The solid state is ice. It is possible to change water to steam or to ice. It is also possible to change steam to water, and to change ice to water.

a. TO CHANGE WATER TO STEAM BY USING HEAT. Put about two inches of water in a teakettle and place it on a hot plate or other source of heat. If a teakettle is not available, a tin can may be used. After the water has been heating for a short time, tiny water droplets should be visible just beyond the end of the teakettle spout. This is like a little cloud. Between the visible water droplets and the spout of the teakettle is a clear space. This clear area is steam. Caution children not to put their hand in the steam, for it will burn them.

By using heat the liquid, water, was changed into a gas, steam.

b. TO CHANGE WATER TO ICE BY TAKING AWAY HEAT. Cold is the absence of heat. So if enough heat is taken from water, it will become ice. If it is freezing weather, put a small pan of water just outside the window and watch it freeze. If the weather is warmer, put a small pan of water or an ice cube tray of water in the freezing compartment of an electric refrigerator. It may be desirable to talk about this at school and ask the children to do the experiment at home.

Sometimes we make use of the fact that freezing water gives up heat. In some regions it may freeze at night and the temperature rise above freezing by ten o'clock the next morning. In these regions, when a freeze is expected, some people cover the plants in their flower beds with papers or burlap bags. Then they thoroughly wet the papers or bags. When the water freezes, heat is given off and the plants do not freeze. Tubs of water may also be placed in green houses or cellars to

Water

help protect against freezing. When the water freezes, it loses eighty calories of heat per cubic centimeter.

c. TO CHANGE STEAM TO WATER BY TAKING AWAY HEAT. Again boil water in a teakettle. Hold a metal cup or china saucer just at the edge of the steam for a few minutes. Remove the cup or saucer and examine it for water droplets.

Water droplets are formed in the area just beyond the steam. The only reason for using the cup or saucer is to make the water condense more quickly. What happened? When the steam strikes the cool air or a cool object like the cup or saucer, it is cooled. When steam is cooled, it becomes liquid water again.

d. TO CHANGE ICE TO WATER BY ADDING HEAT. Put an ice cube in a tin can, sauce pan or pyrex dish. Place the container on a stove or near a warm radiator. If the sun is shining, put another ice cube in the sun. What happens? The ice, frozen water, changes to liquid water. If children are doing this in the winter when there is snow, they might like to use snow in place of ice cubes.

When ice changes to water, it takes heat from whatever is near it. This is the principle used in ice refrigeration. As the ice melts it takes heat from the air and objects near it. Since the absence of heat results in cold, objects near melting ice become cold.

Experience W-15. To observe that water in its gaseous form can exert great pressure

Pour about a pint of water into a teakettle. Fit the spout of the teakettle with a cork stopper. The stopper should be put in firmly, but do not force it down too far. Now place the teakettle on a hot plate. When the water gets hot enough to turn to steam, pressure begins to be built up inside the teakettle. When this pressure becomes strong enough, the cork should be forced out.

Steam under pressure has great force. In an open vessel, when water changes to steam it expands about 1600 times its volume. If the steam is confined where it cannot expand, and heating is continued, both its temperature and pressure will increase. Be very careful not to let too much pressure be built up before the stopper blows out. If the water has been boiling for several minutes and the cork has not come out, remove the teakettle from the fire. After it has cooled some, carefully loosen the cork. Again heat the water in the teakettle.

Experience W-16. To observe that water in its solid form, ice, is lighter than the liquid form, water

Place several ice cubes in a pan of water. What happens? They float.

Why is this important? Do you live near a lake that freezes over in the winter? If so, you know that only the top several inches are solid ice. Below that is water. Fish, other animals, and plants are alive beneath the covering of ice. If ice were heavier than water, lakes would freeze from the bottom up and everything in them would freeze. Also, it is unlikely that the ice would melt completely in the summer. In time, much of the earth would become a desert of ice.

As water gets cold it gets heavier. That is, it gets heavier until it reaches it maximum density at about 39°F. Then as it cools to 32°F., it expands, is lighter, and becomes solid. It will now float on the warmer water.

Experience W-17. To observe that water expands when it freezes

The expansion of water as it freezes is discussed in part *b* of Experience S-12, page 73.

Experience W-18. To observe that warm water rises

Fill one milk bottle with cold water. Drop several drops of ink or vegetable dye in another milk bottle and fill the bottle with hot water. Now cover with a card the mouth of the milk bottle containing cold water. Invert this bottle over the mouth of the bottle containing hot water and carefully slide the card out from between the openings of the two bottles.

The colored, hot water should be seen to move up into the cold water.

Another way to show the same thing is to fill a large glass container with cold water. Be sure that the container has an opening large enough to put a hand down inside. Find a small bottle with a narrow neck such as some kinds of ink bottles and fill it with hot water. Add a little ink or other coloring. Cover the opening of the small bottle and lower it into the container of cold water. Remove the covering. The hot, colored water will flow up and out into the cold water.

FILMS ON AIR AND WATER

You may find the following 16 mm. films a valuable supplement to your work in science.

Air All About Us. 1955, 10 min., sound, black and white, and color. Coronet Films, Coronet Bldg., Chicago 1. Experiments to show the basic concepts of air.

Air Around Us. 1954, 11 min., sound, black and white. Encyclopedia Britannica Films, Inc., 1150 Wilmette Ave., Wilmette, Ill. An introduction to the study of air, with experiments to show some of its properties.

Treasures in Snow. 1956, 6 min., sound, black and white, and color. Moody Institute of Science, 11428 Santa Monica Blvd., West Los Angeles 25, Calif. Discusses snow and explains evaporation, condensation, dew point, and crystallization.

Water Cycle. 1947, 10 min., sound, black and white. Encyclopedia Britannica Films, Inc., 1150 Wilmette Ave., Wilmette, Ill. Shows the movements of water from oceans to sky to rain to streams and rivers and back to oceans.

Weather. 1951, 10 min., sound, black and white. Gateway Productions, Inc., 1859 Powell St., San Francisco 11, Calif. Primary film showing change in the weather, and the reasons for wind, heat, clouds, and rain.

CHAPTER SIX

Ideas in Review

Now that you have explored the content of this booklet, have you started to make progress in developing a feeling of adequacy in working with children in the area of science? Are you eager to start—or perhaps already trying some of the things you have read about? It is hoped that your answer to each of these questions is YES. For if it is, you and your children will have fun exploring, testing, and learning new and exciting things about your environment.

Perhaps it will be helpful to have a brief review of some of the ideas which we have developed and which may influence the way you work with children in the area of science. The organization of this review is designed to help you keep your primary focus on children and also to remind you of ways you can help them to learn.

Children learn through direct experiences. You will, therefore, want to provide. . . .

. . . many opportunities for all children to participate in the *doing* part of science.

. . . simple equipment which children can handle with ease and safety.

. . . a place in the classroom where individual children can repeat and retest the experiences of others, and where the thinking through and the testing out of new ideas and ways of working will be encouraged (this provision should be for all children, not just those considered gifted in science.

. . . opportunities to repeat experiences in different contexts in order to help build concepts concerning interrelationships

Ideas in Review

    (for example, freezing water may be studied as one of the ways rocks are weathered, as one of the three states of water, and as one of the few substances that expand as they freeze).

- . . . opportunities for various kinds of experiences outside the classroom by individuals, small groups, and the total group.
- . . . numerous experiences that will help all children to grow in their ability not only to make careful observations but also to see with understanding.
- . . . opportunities for and encouragement of the creative use of various media for recording and sharing observations.
- . . . experiences that will help children to learn when and how to use all of their senses (for example, one should not: stare directly at the sun without protecting his eyes, purposely listen to loud explosions without protecting his ears, taste unknown substances, inhale deeply an unknown substance, feel the texture of poison ivy leaves, or feel of a kitten by squeezing it with both hands).

Children learn through the experiences of others. You will, therefore, want to provide . . .

- . . . many opportunities for resource persons within the community to share with your boys and girls.
- . . . a wide variety of books and other printed materials so that the children may learn from the experts they cannot meet.
- . . . pictures, slides, filmstrips, and films which will reveal new, unusual, beautiful and interesting things in the world with which many children cannot have firsthand experiences (some of these may also be used to suggest ideas for consideration and to reinforce ideas and learnings which have resulted from class discussions and exploration).
- . . . a stimulus for the constructive use of radio and television.

Children learn from the behavior of teachers and other adults. You will, therefore, want to demonstrate by your own behavior that you think it is important to . . .

- . . . feel that each individual is important and that he has a contribution to make to the group.

... help each individual feel that he is accepted and loved for what he is and that, although the results of his thinking and acting may sometimes be rejected, this does not mean a loss of acceptance or love.

... realize that individuals are alike in many ways and unlike in many ways, so that the members of the group will work together sometimes and individually at other times.

... realize that each individual grows and learns at his own unique rate.

... realize that each child in the group has strengths as well as weaknesses, and that each can learn and each can teach.

... use many resources to find information about things and phenomena being discussed or observed.

... remain continually alert for accounts of new discoveries and of reorganized thinking about hypotheses, theories, and generally accepted facts.

... always seek the most accurate information available.

... maintain an open mind toward any new evidence which may require reorganization of earlier accepted information.

... examine evidence and evaluate statements rather than blindly accepting everything that a status person or a so-called authority says or writes.

... practice safe ways of working with both living and non-living things.

... give good care to living things taken from the natural habitat.

... feel a responsibility for the care and wise use of all parts of the natural environment.

As is clearly evident to you, this booklet is not intended to be a complete treatment of all of the ways in which children learn about science or of all the content of the field of science. Rather, it is hoped that some of the ideas included here will be helpful in checking your plans for work with children in the area of science, and that an occasional rereading of these ideas will function as a helpful stimulus in your everyday striving to provide rich and varied experiences for your boys and girls.

Bibliography

Allee, W. C.; Emerson, Alfred E.; Park, Orlando; Park, Thomas; Schmidt, Karl P. *Principles of Animal Ecology.* Philadelphia: W. B. Saunders Company, 1949.
Arey, Charles K. *Science Experiences for Elementary Schools.* New York: Bureau of Publications, Teachers College, Columbia University, 1942.
Bennett, Hugh H. *Elements of Soil Conservation.* 2nd Edition. New York: McGraw-Hill Book Company, Inc., 1955.
Blough, Glenn O.; Blackwood, Paul E. *Teaching Elementary Science.* Washington, D. C.: U. S. Office of Education, Bulletin No. 4, 1948.
Blough, Glenn O.; Huggett, Albert J. *Elementary-School Science and How to Teach It.* New York: Dryden Press, 1951.
Burnett, R. Will. *Teaching Science in the Elementary School.* New York: Rinehart and Company, Inc., 1953.
Craig, Gerald S. *Science for the Elementary-School Teacher.* Boston: Ginn and Company, 1947.
Dice, Lee R. *Natural Communities.* Ann Arbor: University of Michigan Press, 1952.
Freeman, K.; Dowling, T. I.; Lacy, N.; and Tippett, J. S. *Helping Children Understand Science.* Philadelphia: John C. Winston Company, 1954.
Garrison, Charlotte G. *Science Experiences for Little Children.* New York: Charles Scribner's Sons, 1939.
Greenlee, Julian. *Teaching Science to Children.* Dubuque, Iowa: Wm. C. Brown Co., 1951.
King, Thomas. *Water—Miracle of Nature.* New York: Macmillan Company, 1953.
Longwell, Chester R.; Knopf, Adolph; Flint, Richard F. *Physical Geology.* 3rd Edition. New York: John Wiley and Sons, Inc., 1948.
Lynde, Carleton J. *Science Experiences with Home Equipment.* 2nd Edition. Scranton: International Textbook Company, 1950.
Lynde, Carleton J. *Science Experiences with Inexpensive Equipment.* 2nd Edition. Scranton: International Textbook Company, 1950.
Lynde, Carleton J. *Science Experiences with Ten-cent Store Equipment.* 2nd Edition. Scranton: International Textbook Company, 1950.
National Education Association, Department of Elementary School Principals. *Science for Today's Children.* Thirty-second Yearbook, Volume XXXIII, Number I. Washington, D. C.: The Association, 1953.
National Society for the Study of Education. *Science in the Elementary School.* Forty-sixth Yearbook, Part I, Section II. Chicago: University of Chicago Press, 1947.
Von Engeln, O. D.; Caster, Kenneth. *Geology.* New York: McGraw-Hill Book Company, 1952.
Wilson, Carl L. *Botany.* New York: Dryden Press, 1952.

Equipment Supply Houses

Carolina Biological Supply Company, Elon College, North Carolina.
: Living and preserved materials.

Central Scientific Company, 1700 Irving Park Boulevard, Chicago, Illinois.
: General equipment.

Chicago Apparatus Company, 1735-1743 North Ashland Avenue, Chicago, Illinois.
: General equipment.

Fisher Scientific Company, 711-723 Forbes Street, Pittsburgh, Pennsylvania.
: General equipment.

General Biological Supply House, 8200 South Hoyne Avenue, Chicago 20, Illinois.
: Living and preserved materials.

Hoeltge Bros., Inc., 1919-1921 Gest Street, Cincinnati 4, Ohio.
: Laboratory animal cages and equipment.

New York Scientific Supply Company, Inc., 28 West 30th Street, New York 1, New York.
: Preserved and living materials, and chemicals.

Science Kit, Inc., Tonawanda, New York.
: General equipment.

Southern Scientific Company, Inc., Atlanta 3, Georgia.
: General equipment.

Stansi Scientific Co., 1231 North Honore Street, Chicago 22, Illinois.
: General equipment.

Ward's Natural Science Establishment, Inc., 3000 Ridge Road East, Rochester 9, New York.
: Living and preserved materials, rocks, and fossils.

W. M. Welch Scientific Company, 1515 Sedgewick Street, Chicago 10, Illinois.
: General equipment.